Naked

European-Atlantic Publications Ltd

Naked Science

Chris Smith

E - A P

First published in Great Britain in 2006 by
European-Atlantic Publications Ltd
4 St Pauls Way
London
N3 2PP
www.e-ap.co.uk

A CIP catalogue record for this book is available from the
British Library.

ISBN: 1-905770-01-4
(ISBN-13:) 978-1-905770-01-4

Edited by Mike Darton
Cover art work: Adrian Teal
Cover design: David Siddall

Typeset in Great Britain by Kerrypress Ltd

Printed and bound in the United Kingdom by
Bookmarque Ltd, Croydon, Surrey

Acknowledgements

Science isn't just for corduroy-clad geeks and anoraks with shocking teeth, crazy hair and glasses stronger than the Hubble Space Telescope – it's something that affects all of us and will almost certainly change your life.

But above all, as Australia's Dr Karl Kruszelnicki said to me recently, 'Science is like sex – it might have practical results, but that's not why we do it.'

That's the motto of this book, which is intended to strip down science to the bare essentials and expose you to what science really is – addictively fun, interesting, and occasionally a bit naughty.

Naked Science is based upon the musings of The Naked Scientist, my alter-ego and radio show. But I couldn't have begun to reveal all to the world, at least scientifically speaking, without the help of a few amazing people who have nurtured my scientific naturism over the last few years.

They include Margaret Hyde, Tim Gillett and Graham Hughes from the BBC eastern region, Howard Benson at Five Live, Dr Karl, the Winston Churchill Memorial Trust, and everyone at ABC Radio National including Tim Latham, Steven Turner, Fran Kelly, David Fisher and Polly Rickard (who bakes amazing cakes).

I am also indebted to the wonderful people at Cambridge University, where I work, including Stacey Efstathiou, Tony Minson and Andrew Wyllie, and my assistant, Anna Lacey, who is organised beyond belief and talks nearly as much as I do!

I am also eternally grateful to Jem Rashbass, who was instrumental in getting the ball rolling in the early days, Tim Wreghitt, who encouraged me to write a book and even found me a publisher, and Brian Tomes and Boris Andonov from E-AP, two of the nicest people I've ever met.

Lastly, I have to thank the person who catalysed the whole process, the ABC's ex-*Dr-Who*-extra, Robyn Williams, without whom I would be nowhere.

To:

My wonderful family, Sarah, Jacky and Richard, for making it possible.

And my wonderful friends Margaret, Tim and Robyn, for making it happen.

STRIPPING DOWN SCIENCE TO THE BARE ESSENTIALS

Take an onion, chop it finely, add water, half a pint of washing-up liquid (lemon-scented variety optional), a hand–ful of salt, and simmer at 60°C (140°F) for 10–20 minutes. Pour the attractive-smelling mixture through a coffee-filter and collect the juice. Cool, add fresh pineapple juice, and incubate at body temperature for 10 minutes. Meanwhile, chill some aftershave that you hate in the freezer, then gently pour twice the volume of frozen aftershave over a sample of the onion/pineapple *jus*. Before your eyes a disgustingly glutinous substance begins to appear.

This is the recipe for extracting large amounts of DNA from an onion using simple ingredients you can find at home. It's also the recipe that got the *Naked Scientists* started on the radio.

I've always been very keen on science, and particularly on talking to people about it, so when someone emailed me asking if I would be willing to help out at the Cambridge Science Festival by giving a talk or demonstrating something, I jumped at the chance.

It was early 1999, I was half way through my PhD, and the GM-food debacle was in full swing. The letters DNA were spattered across every medium; there were newspapers deco-rated with double helixes – some of which were even spiraling the wrong way – and pictures of Frankenstein eating dodgy-looking tomatoes. The general public were terrified that they were about to fall victim to another BSE crisis and shoppers everywhere were eschewing the Jolly Green Giant on the offchance that he used to be a lot smaller before someone tinkered with his DNA. But from talking to people, it was pretty clear that most hadn't the faintest idea what DNA is, or even what it looks like, let alone how it works, so this seemed like the perfect opportunity to show them.

I set up the onion-DNA demonstration a bit like a cooking programme and invited members of the audience to 'come on down' and help with the procedure. While volunteers vigorously sliced and diced, blinking red-eyed through the onion vapour, we gave a short talk on the nuts and bolts of life's recipe-book including how DNA was discovered, how it copies itself, how it is organised into chromosomes, and how it encodes gene products which do useful things in cells. The end result was a spectacular handful of onion DNA, a rapt audience for whom we were able to debunk many of the inflammatory myths being peddled by the mass media, and a phonecall from a local commercial radio station inviting me for an interview.

I took along a colleague to the radio station for moral support. Between us we managed to turn what was supposed to have been a five-minute interview about DNA into two hours of light-hearted scientific banter, punctuated by regular music breaks. The radio station were sufficiently impressed to risk asking us back again a week later, and from there the concept that became the *Naked Scientists* was born.

Initially, we appeared as guests on someone else's show, but quite quickly it became clear that to realise the true potential of what we were doing, we would need our own show. As luck would have it, at around the same time the Biotechnology and Biological Sciences Research Council (BBSRC) launched a new scheme to promote public understanding of science and were calling for applicants. I negotiated to buy a year's airtime from the radio station at a very reduced rate, and we wrote a grant application to the BBSRC to pay for it. It was quite a gamble for a couple of PhD students, not least because we were staring clinical finals and thesis-writing in the face. But the great god of radio was obviously smiling benevolently on the new millennium because in January 2000 the BBSRC agreed to fund our project, and the show, which we christened *ScienceWorld*, was on the road.

I'm certain we sounded terrible to begin with. The transition from guest to show host is a difficult one. You suddenly have to worry about playing ads and jingles at the correct times, getting the levels right, answering the phone, and all the time you're trying to talk intelligently about complicated subjects and keep the conversation going.

Although the learning curve was steep we improved rapidly and before long it was really starting to hang together. We turned the show into a light-hearted look at what was happening each week in the world of science, technology and medicine, and interspersed the chat with popular chart music. We were succeeding in dishing out 'household-interest-radio'-type material to a 'pop-music-radio'-type audience who would probably not normally be exposed to educational science radio programming. To keep people listening we also included a few funny stories each week – like the one about a Reliant Robin seen parked all over York with an industrial-sized sack of potatoes in the passenger seat. It turned out that the driver weighed over 220 kilograms [490 pounds; 35 stone] and, without the counterbalancing effect of the potatoes, the three-wheeled car was prone to rolling over on bends. Naturally, we used this story to highlight the importance of eating a balanced diet ...

Gratifyingly, the audience began to grow and we were seeing the number of people tuned to the station jumping by 50 to 100% when we came on air. More and more people were phoning in for the competition and to ask us questions – clearly Halford's car-care kits and Geri Halliwell CDs (which were all we had to give away) must have been in demand in Cambridge at that time, although I prefer to think that people genuinely enjoyed calling in to take part!

By the end of the series the radio station had been taken over by a new company, but because our ratings spoke for themselves we were offered the chance to carry on and make another series of the show. And because we all had deadlines looming – including a thesis to complete and clinical finals – we took six months off to get everything finished.

During this time I wrote another grant application to the BBSRC asking for support for a further series, and funding to develop a website to act as an online companion to the radio show. The idea was to maximise the reach and educational potential of the material being generated for each show by archiving it in text and audio formats on the web so that anyone, anywhere, anytime, could listen to it, or read it. I also realised we needed a sexier name which clearly defined us as an anorak-free zone. While I was trying to write a particularly challenging part of my thesis the name 'Naked Scientists' drifted into my head. It seemed like the perfect choice – it was slightly naughty, it made people laugh, it clearly said 'geek-free', and best of all, the domain name was unclaimed on the Internet!

The BBSRC were kind enough to grant us another year's support so, after my finals, I built our website – www.thenakedscientists.com – in two weeks flat over the summer (largely thanks to a lot of help from CARET at Cambridge University and a large jar of Nescafé), and The Naked Scientists Radio Show then hit the airwaves for the first time in the autumn of 2001.

For the new series we focused the show not just on science news stories but on an interview with a guest scientist too. We signed up Richard Dawkins, DNA fingerprinting-inventor Alec Jeffreys, Susan Greenfield, Steve Jones (who told me I share 60% of my genes with a banana), and even James Watson. The audience loved it – and, it turned out, so did the competition.

The BBC had been listening to us for a while and called up mid-series to invite me over for a 'chat' which culminated in an offer to move the next series of the show to BBC Cambridgeshire. This would see us grow from talking to a few thousand people around the city and outlying villages, to talking to a whole county.

By this time it was obvious that we were on to something. The website was taking a quarter of a million hits – admittedly, many of them on account of the word 'naked', but at least we couldn't be accused of preaching to the converted – and emails were coming in from people all around the world who were enjoying listening to our shows. It was clear that what we were doing had the potential to be much bigger.

But having never had any training in radio or communication, I couldn't help thinking that I lacked the experience and credibility required to drive a project like this forward to reach greater heights, and bigger audiences.

Having drawn a blank in my search for the necessary experience at home, I decided to look to Australia. I had made contact with the Australian Broadcasting Corporation (ABC), and through them, with probably the best science radio journalist in the business, Robyn Williams (whose other claim to fame is as an extra in *Dr Who* many many moons ago).

I ended up meeting Robyn in late 2002 in a dingy hotel in London, where he was staying while visiting the BA Festival of Science. I told him what I'd been up to, and that I'd like to learn a bit more, and he immediately offered to arrange for me to go to Sydney in 2004.

The only thing missing was the minor matter of money. Fortunately, there is a wonderful organisation called the Winston Churchill Memorial Trust (www.wcmt.org.uk) which was established as a living memory to Winston Churchill upon his death, and now offers 'the opportunity of a lifetime' to successful applicants who want to do something 'life-changing'.

In late 2002 I applied to the Churchill Trust for support to join the Radio Science Unit at ABC Radio National, Australia, and after a testing interview with a panel of 'greats' including neurologist Dr Roger Bannister, the first four-minute-mile runner, I was awarded a fellowship.

In the meantime, being the only person from my home county to win a Churchill Fellowship that year, the press release of successful applicants released by the Trust was picked up by BBC Essex who invited me along to take part in *Tea at 3, with Steve* to talk on air about what I was up to.

While I was there I took the opportunity to play some of our previous shows to the BBC Essex director of programming, Tim Gillett. Two days later he phoned to say that when the new series started in Cambridge, they would like to broadcast it simultaneously on BBC Essex, potentially tripling our audience. Furthermore, he wondered whether I would like to make some special two-hour-long bank holiday programmes for them.

The prospect of running a two-hour live science show, on an untried audience, at peak time, at a radio station I'd visited only once, and with the potential to fall flat on my face, was buttock-clenchingly scary. But before I had a chance to have second thoughts, I heard myself replying 'That'll be wonderful, thank you.'

Thankfully, my initial fears evaporated when those shows were broadcast live at peak time in May and August 2003. They drew an enormous audience response; people of all ages from 9 to 90 phoned in with questions like 'How many pieces of toast can you make with the energy in a lightning bolt?', 'Why does my car do 8 miles to the gallon more with an air filter full of mothballs?', and 'How many organs can I donate and remain alive?' They were certainly one of the most enjoyable experiences I've had with this project, mainly because I suddenly realised what it could achieve. Another major benefit of our success on BBC Essex was that the managing editor, a wonderful lady called Margaret Hyde, was sufficiently impressed by what we were doing that she persuaded all of the other BBC radio stations in the region, with a potential audience of 6 million, to take the new series from September 2003.

And so it was that we ended up broadcasting not just to one county but to the entire BBC eastern region, and live onto the Internet. We picked up listeners all over the world including people in Australia, Canada, California, and even Japan – one young lady in Tokyo phoned in to ask why crying makes your eyes go red. She defiantly told our telephone operator 'You'd better put me on the show because I've stayed up until 4am to call you!'

We are now in our second series on the BBC. We paused for six months at the start of 2004 while I took up my Winston Churchill Fellowship and joined Robyn Williams at the ABC in Sydney for six months. This was probably the most important six months of my life in the media. While I was there, in addition to making programmes about landmine-detecting GM cress plants, and the origins of HIV, I began contributing live science commentaries to the Radio National Breakfast programme each Monday morning. The ABC team were obviously pleased with the result because they asked me to carry on once I had returned to the UK. So every Thursday night, with a twinge of nostalgia, I am patched into the Sydney studio, where it's Friday morning, to talk science from Cambridge for 10 minutes. It's a very strange feeling to be talking to a whole country on the other side of the world, but it just goes to show how universal science, and our interest in it, has become.

Physics
Games and pastimes

Oh no! Goal! Why didn't the goalkeeper anticipate where the ball was going?

It's official: we mustn't blame the goalie (or at least, not always) for letting in a curved ball – scientists have proved that the brain just cannot process the trajectory of spinning balls! Psychologist Cathy Craig, from Queen's University, Belfast, first began studying the problem after watching soccer player Roberto Carlos score for Brazil in 1997. 'Everybody thought it was going wide, but it curved in at the last minute,' she said. To investigate why even professionals seem so poor at predicting where the curved ball will end up she asked players to predict where the ball would end up in a series of virtual reality shots on a display screen. The ball watched by participants had an added spin of 600 revolutions per minute. The outcome was that even the pros were unable to correctly predict the path that the ball would take. A spinning ball generates an effect called the Magnus force which causes it to follow a curved path. But because such an effect does not occur naturally, we haven't evolved a visual mechanism to process it, as we have for anticipating the effects of gravity. So it seems the keeper's off the hook – for *those* misses, anyway!

Communications
Medicine

So romantic to have a quiet drink together – but what if we are far apart?

Absence makes the heart grow fonder, and now a pair of Wi-Fi drinking glasses could help to bring separated loved ones closer together, according to Boston-based researchers at MIT's Media Lab. Inventors Jackie Lee and Hyemin Chung have incorporated a variety of coloured LEDs, liquid sensors and Wi-Fi links into a pair of tallish tumblers. When one drinker picks up his or her glass, red LEDs in the partner's glass switch on, and when one of the pair puts a glass to his or her lips, white LEDs glow up around the rim of the other glass so showing that the partner has taken a sip. The inventors claim that their wireless glasses help people feel that they are sharing an intimate drinking experience together, even when one of them is on the other side of the world. But more practically, the technology could also prove useful in the setting of a hospital or a care institution to check that patients or elderly and infirm people are drinking enough water. The 'lover's cups', as they have been christened, were unveiled at the Montreal CHI 2006 Conference on Computer-Human Interaction.

Factoid:
'Sound travels twice as fast in air as it does in water.'
FALSE
Sound waves actually travel four times *slower* in air than in water.

Human biology
Sleep

What's worse – to wake up to an alarm clock or to replace one you've smashed?

Are you one of those people with an alarm-clock allergy or a penchant for the snooze button? MIT's media lab think they might have the answer to your bed-loving tendencies with 'Clocky', an alarm clock on wheels that runs off! As soon as you hit the snooze button to silence Clocky, he zooms off to a random hiding-place elsewhere in the room, forcing you to get up and find him to shut him up. The ensuing hunt should force even the most bed-fast individual to eschew the sheets and head for the shower!

Sociology

Is it really possible to read other people like a book?

A library in Sweden has decided to combine the lending of books and records with the lending of human storytellers. So far nine people – including a gypsy, a journalist and a homosexual – have been 'archived' in the collection. 'Readers' pop into the library and borrow the individual for a half-hour chat about their life, beliefs and values in a nearby cafe. Apparently, the main idea is to let people come face to face with their prejudices!

Geology
Palaeontology

Wasn't there a time when greenhouse gases were not only useful but essential?

A whiff of methane has helped Japanese researchers to sniff out signs of the Earth's earliest life in rock samples from western Australia. Yuichiro Ueno and his colleagues at the Tokyo Institute of Technology studied samples of quartz collected from a geological feature called the Dresser Formation, which dates back about 3½ billion years and consists of pillows of lava containing vertical quartz seams topped by sedimentary rocks. Under a microscope the quartz appears stuffed with tiny time-capsules in the form of bubbles of water and gas trapped when the rocks were first deposited. By crushing them open, the Japanese team were able to collect and analyse the ancient gases, and by studying their chemical composition, find out where they came from. Their results show that the bubbles contain a lot of methane that bears the chemical signature of life, indicating that some of the Earth's earliest inhabitants were methane-producing microbes. Specifically, the methane the researchers found is in a form referred to as 'C13-depleted', which is a hallmark of life because micro-organisms are known to be fussy and prefer to use the lighter C12 isotope of carbon. So we now know that some of the earliest organisms flourishing on the Earth were producers of the greenhouse gas methane, and researchers think that they may have made a big contribution to keeping the planet warm because in those days the sun emitted less heat energy than it does today.

Diseases and disorders
Medicine

Multiple sclerosis remains all too common: is there any prospect of effective therapy?

Researchers in the USA have come up with a novel way to tackle the debilitating neurological disease multiple sclerosis (MS). In patients with the disease the immune system mounts an attack on a substance in the brain called myelin which covers and encloses nerve fibres rather like the insulating material surrounding an electrical cable. Damage to this myelin coat prevents affected nerve fibres from transmitting information correctly, which causes sufferers to develop problems with their vision, speech, sensation and movements. This damaging immune attack is driven by a population of renegade white blood cells, but putting anything but a temporary stop to the terroristic tendencies of these cells has proved difficult in the past. Now researchers believe that the cells might hold the key to their own downfall. They have created a personalised vaccine by collecting sample cells from patients with MS, damaging the cells with a dose of radiation, and then re-injecting them. In this way the immune system is trained to recognise the appearance of the defective cells, and kill them. Because the healthy versions of these same cells also carry the same markers on their surfaces, they are taken down too, stopping the MS in its tracks. It's early days, but in a small trial run by PharmaFrontiers, the company behind the vaccine, amongst 15 MS patients who received the new treatment, the rate of flare-ups was reduced by 92%. A larger study involving 150 patients, 100 of whom will receive the active vaccine and 50 a placebo, is currently under way. Researchers are interpreting the results with caution, however, because no vaccines yet produced have been shown to successfully modify the course of MS.

Domestic events

Aargh! Why has my best white shirt come out of the washing all pink?

Because – regrettably not for the first time, dumbo – you'd inadvertently left an old red sock hidden among the pile of your whites washing. But colours that run in the wash may be a thing of the past if a new idea from Procter & Gamble pays off. The company have come up with the notion of using substances called polymeric amines which can be added to the wash to mop up dye that leaches into the washwater, before it can stain clothes. These new molecules are insoluble, so the company proposes to impregnate them into loose-weave towels which you add to the wash alongside your washing, where they soak up any rogue dyes. Once they change colour, you throw them away.

Forensic science
Human biology

Can science give us a new hands-on approach to fingerprinting?

Researchers have come up with a novel way to non-destructively lift fingerprints from a variety of previously 'un-fingerprintable' surfaces – like skin – by using X-rays. As well as fingerprints, the new approach will also pick up chemical signatures present at a crime scene (including, for instance, gunpowder or explosives), providing extra clues to the activities of the culprit.

The senses
Domestic events

Do you mean farmyard smells, or are you just trying to avoid talking bullsh*t?

Researchers George Preti and Charles Wysocki, from Philadelphia's Monell Chemical Senses Center, have hit upon a way to make the lives of people who live near farms more bearable at times of the year when farmers fertilise their land the natural way. They have come up with a chemical that makes you think that manure smells nice! It's been known for some time that when an odour is present for a long period of time the nose learns to ignore it, a process called 'adaptation'. But certain chemicals can also fool the nose into ignoring other smells too, termed 'cross-adaptation', and this is the approach taken by the Monell scientists. They first tracked down the identity of the molecules that make manure hard to live with, and then set about testing pleasant-smelling chemicals to find examples capable of 'blinding' the nose to the *bouquet d'ordure*. They eventually tracked down the perfect example – the ethyl-ester of 3-methyl-2-octanoic acid – which, when added to manure, can counteract its odour. Naturally, the smell still reaches your nose, but you just don't notice it. If combined with other odour-combating chemicals, say the scientists, it could make a smell of a difference to life downwind of the farm at fertilising time.

Genetics
Pregnancy and maternity

They said cloning would become common, but it hasn't turned out like that. Why not?

One finding that might help to explain why cloning remains a highly hit-and-miss affair has been produced by a team of scientists at the University of Missouri, Columbia. They have pinpointed how a developing embryo determines what cells will become the foetus, and which cells will form the placental lifeline linking the baby to its mother. By studying fertilised mouse eggs, Michael Roberts and his team found that when the egg divides for the first time, the products of a gene called Cdx2 make their way to the nucleus, where the DNA is located, in just *one* of the two cells. As the embryo develops, this cell and its descendants go on to give rise to the placenta and umbilical cord, whereas the other cell, without any Cdx2 in its nucleus, forms the baby. To prove that they were on the right track the researchers injected the cells containing Cdx2 with substances that could stop the gene from operating. Embryos treated in this way failed to produce a placenta. The team also found that in eggs yet to be fertilised the products of the Cdx2 gene were preferentially localised on just one side of each egg, so that when an egg was fertilised and began to divide, one of the daughter cells inherited the Cdx2 products and the other did not. This finding turns on its head our traditional belief that, at early stages at least, all the cells in an embryo are equal, and may help to improve the efficiency of current cloning techniques.

X-ray technology

How can modern technology recover ancient writings thought lost forever?

The Archimedes Palimpsest is the oldest surviving transcript of the work of the ancient Greek mathematician Archimedes. It was laboriously copied out as a manuscript in the tenth century but, unfortunately, during the twelfth century a pious owner recycled it into a prayer book by scraping off the ink and replacing maths with miracles! Luckily, thanks to modern technology it is now possible to read it again, a thousand years later, with the help of X-rays. Scientists at the Stanford Synchrotron radiation laboratory, in the USA, used a beam of concentrated X-rays produced by a particle accelerator to see through the prayers, and twentieth-century repair work, to disclose the original text beneath. The technique works by exciting iron atoms in remnants of the original ink, causing them to glow and create a sharp image.

Factoid:
'Chalk in cliffs like the White Cliffs of Dover is made up of the fossils of tiny animals.'

FALSE
The chalk is made up of the calcium carbonate shells that tiny animals called cocolithophores accreted around themselves when they lived in the sea 70 million years ago during the Cretaceous Period. On the death of a cocolithophore, its shell would disintegrate into separate chalky disks and sink to become part of the sediment on the sea bed.

Sociology
Communications

... And furthermore, I must just go on to say that – Hello? Are you awake?

Researchers at the Massachusetts Insitute of Technology (MIT) Media Lab are developing a mobile boredom detector designed to clip onto a pair of glasses and warn wearers if they are boring the pants off (or maybe only annoying) the people they meet. The device is the brainchild of MIT's Rana El Kaliouby, and she hopes in particular that it will make life easier for people with autism who have trouble interpreting the body language of others. It works by relaying images of the facial expressions made by people chatting to the wearer to a hand-held computer which analyses the pictures and picks out how the individual is responding to the conversation. Specifically, the software focuses on movements of the eyebrows, lips and nose, and also tracks nods and shakes of the head, and head tilting – changes which indicate boredom or a less than equable frame of mind. If it spots any of these, the hand-held computer vibrates, alerting the user to change tack or draw the conversation to a close. The researchers trained the computer by showing it over 100 eight-second video clips of actors displaying specific emotions. Now, when presented with prevously unseen video clips, the system correctly predicts people's emotions 90% of the time when analysing actors, and 64% of the time when looking at shots of ordinary people. The researchers are now training their software with footage from movies and webcams, and working on a way to shrink the camera and the hand-held computer to a comfortable size.

Food

Diseases and disorders

Do you feel as bad as I do? Was it the chicken salad we had for lunch, do you think?

Every year in the UK at least 10 million unfortunate victims end up locked to a toilet seat thanks to something they ate – the figures for Australia are proportionately similar: about 2 million people annually – and poultry is a common culprit. That's because chickens and other birds often carry pathogenic bacteria which, if the meat is not carefully prepared, can infect the consumer. To combat the problem researcher Billy Hargis is giving his chickens a dose of probiotic 'good bacteria' – similar to the yoghurts on sale in the health food store – in a bid to cut the potential for food poisoning due to bugs like *Salmonella* and *Campylobacter*. The idea is that the good bacteria will compete for nutrients and resources, pushing out the harmful gut pathogens. To isolate them in the first place, Hargis's team collect the natural bacterial flora from healthy chickens, confirm that the bugs they have isolated can compete effectively against the pathogen, grow them up, and then administer them to chicks in their feed and water. Also adding prebiotics – substances which encourage the growth of the good bacteria – to the diet helps to maintain a thriving intestinal population. At the moment the researchers are currently working to achieve the perfect cocktail of good bacteria, but the fruits of their labours have now been embraced by a number of commercial poultry farmers eager to cut the levels of food poisoning bacteria in their produce.

Space
Human biology

Are you *sure* 'muscle tone' is not just astronaut-speak for 'sun tan lotion'?

Scientists at the University of California have come up with a novel way to prevent the muscles of astronauts from wasting away under micro-gravity conditions – with a 'space cycle'. Essentially a human-powered centrifuge, researcher Vincent Caiozzo's machine generates artificial gravity by turning in a circle and carries two astronauts at a time. One pedals on a bike, to drive the device, while the other stands on a platform performing squat-thrusts against the 'gravity' generated by his companion. The space cycle, which can be fitted with any kind of exercise equipment, provides the equivalent of an off-world multi-gym and means that even in zero gravity astronauts can still exercise under gravitational conditions.

Computer technology
Electronics

Flat LCD screens are now standard – so what's next? Folding? Concertina-style?

Folding, nothing! Philips are planning to roll out their roll-up computer screens in 2007. The technical giant has teamed up with the US E-Ink company to produce a 13-centimetre (5-inch) roll-uppable black-and-white computer screen which is only 0.1 millimetre (0.004 inch) thick and rolls up into a tube 15 millimetres (three-fifths of an inch) across.

Ageing
The senses
Human biology

When the elderly fall over, it's not always because they've hit the bottle, is it?

Scientists from the USA have succeeded in helping the elderly to improve their sense of balance, so that it matches that of a 20-year-old, by installing vibrators in the soles of their shoes. The elderly are prone to falls because nerves signalling the position of joints and the contact of the feet with the floor become less sensitive with age. But by using tiny motors to apply vibration to the feet, the researchers were able compensate for the deficient nerve-endings. The researchers suggest that the technique could reduce the approximately one-third of over-65s injured annually by falls.

Buildings
Domestic events

Where on Earth would a crematorium be equipped like a space-age sports stadium?

Where else? Wacky Australians have built a 120-seater crematorium complex complete with state-of-the-art visual technology to help families record funeral services. It also boasts facilities to give musical, video or multimedia presentations, and will even broadcast the proceedings on the Internet so that relatives abroad can participate in a virtual funeral!

Business and litigation

Genetics

A rose by any other name would smell as sweet: what if the other name was 'stinkweed'?

In the first example of its kind, a US cancer-research institute has been threatened with legal action by the makers of the Pokemon card game after one of its researchers borrowed the company's trademark to name a newly discovered gene. Naming the gene after the game would probably not normally have provoked much of a fuss were it not for the fact that Pier Paolo Pandolfi, from the Memorial Sloan-Kettering Cancer Center in New York, had discovered a gene that causes cancer. As a result, news headlines have been springing up around the world along the lines of 'Pokemon causes cancer'. Naturally, the company is concerned about the possible impact this may have on its image and has threatened to sue if the malign gene is not renamed. This is not the first time a scientist has been landed in hot water by naming a gene after a high-street product. In 1993 Cambridge researcher Alfonso Martinez Arias was told to rename his 'Velcro' fly gene after the Velcro Corporation claimed that he was diluting the value of their name and mark. So far, though, US researcher Bob Riddle who named another gene Sonic Hedgehog in 1993 appears to have escaped notice! The Sloan-Kettering scientists have now agreed to rename Pokemon by the slightly less sexy title Zbtb7.

Human biology
Physics

Kung fu? Smashing concrete blocks with one's bare hands? Anybody can do that, surely?

Scientists from the Institute of Physics (IOP) in London are resorting to kung fu to get the message across about science. By smashing through 8-centimetre (3-inch)-thick blocks of concrete with their bare hands, the IOP scientists are hoping to pursuade the public that kung fu is all about physics. The key to successfully breaking a concrete block? You have to supply the absolute maximum kinetic energy, so the strike with the palm of the hand has to be as fast as possible (since kinetic energy is proportional to speed squared); you must get your maximum weight behind it (because kinetic energy is also proportional to the mass); and you have to aim beyond the surface of the block to ensure the absolute maximum strike speed (because otherwise the brain slows the hand down as it nears the concrete surface). And does it hurt? Well, I cannot tell a lie – yes it does. But not half as much as if you stop believing you can break it, and slow your hand down!

Factoid:
'Putting your ear to a railway track can tell you if a train is coming.'

TRUE
Unhappily, however, it cannot tell you which *direction* it is coming from – as a Romanian man found out when placing his ear against the rail to listen for the approach of his train. Demonstrating his technique to a crowd of supposedly impressed onlookers, he was run over by an express train coming the other way.

The senses

Food and drink

Will machines ever be able to replace human tea-tasters or wine-tasters?

Scientists in the Netherlands have built an artificial throat to help speed up the process of testing and synthesising the flavours of drinks. Most of what we call 'taste' is actually down to our noses. Try holding your nose and then placing something strongly tasting in your mouth – you won't be able to 'taste' it – and that's because when we eat or drink something the aromas contained in the food are released inside the mouth and then puffed up into the nose where we 'smell' them. It's the combined sensations produced by both the tongue and the nose that gives something its flavour, but drink flavours are very difficult to get right because liquid spends so little time in the mouth before being swallowed. To solve the problem the Dutch researchers set up two glass tubes, one placed vertically above the other, connected by a short piece of rubber tubing that could be closed with a clamp. The top tube was the 'mouth' while the bottom tube represented the oesophagus (gullet). At the bottom of the model they attached an air supply to blow gas up the tube at the same rate as a normal human exhalation. They added small amounts of flavoured liquid to the 'mouth', then opened the 'throat' (the clamped rubber tube) to simulate swallowing, and once the liquid had drained, turned on the air stream to simulate exhalation. They tested the 'breath' collected from the top of the mouth and analysed it. The researchers found that for all of the flavours they tested the breath analysis from their model precisely matched the aroma profile produced when the same flavour was given to real people to drink.

Electronics
Information technology

Surely it's not possible to get even more information on a disk the size of a DVD?

Just when we were all coming round to the idea of having ditched our long-standing relationship with the video recorder in favour of a state-of-the-art DVD player, researchers at Imperial College, London, have come up with a new design for a digital disk which, despite being the same size as a traditional CD or DVD, will be able to store up to 200 times more information – enough, in fact, to hold every episode of *The Simpsons* ever made, or the complete *Lord of the Rings* trilogy 13 times over. That's about 470 hours of film. Peter Torok and his team, who have come up with the new disk design, have christened their invention MODS (which actually stands for Multiplex Optical Data Storage). Under the microscope, CDs and DVDs consist of a single long groove or track which spirals out from the centre of the disk towards the edge. If you unwound this groove it would stretch about 56 kilometres (35 miles). At regular points along the groove is either a small pit or an area of flat surface. The sequence of these pits and flat areas is used to digitally encode the data on the disk. The new MODS system takes the design a step further. The pits are asymmetrically-shaped and contain a sunken step precisely positioned at one of 332 different angles. The angle of the step in the pit can therefore encode the information, meaning that each pit can carry 10 times more information than on a traditional CD or DVD. The new system will be designed to be reverse-compatible with existing technologies like CDs and DVDs. Critically, it will also enable developers to make much smaller storage devices.

Food

Sound

Other than in an asylum, how do you distinguish between one nut and another?

A bag of pistachio nuts always contains a few unopened specimens, largely because the process used to sort the open from the closed nuts is far from perfect. But now a Kansas-based inventor, Tom Pearson, has come up with a sound way to separate the two – by creating a machine that can tell the difference between the noises made when opened and closed nuts clatter onto a steel tray. Unopened nuts make a shorter ringing sound when they drop onto the tray, compared with their open counterparts, and these unwanted specimens are blown away with a puff of compressed air. Capable of sorting 25 nuts a second, the new machine is slower than the existing technique, which relies on opened nuts being caught by a series of needles as they are spun in drum, but the new technique is 97% accurate, compared with 90% for the needle method. This could save companies up to half a million pounds a year ... and a lot of frustrated customers!

Factoid:
'In London, England, there is a special memorial commemorating all the animals, birds and other creatures that ever made a formal contribution to British military efforts at war.'

TRUE
It is in Park Lane, and included in the sculpted representations are horses, mules, pigeons, dogs, camels, elephants, monkeys, canaries, and even the glow-worms that helped First-World-War trench soldiers read their maps at night!

Human statistics
The senses

Country music is happy-go-lucky and zingy and life-enhancing ... isn't it?

The 2004 'Ig Nobel prize for medicine' – one of a series of awards intended to recognise slightly more unusual research – has been awarded to two US doctors who have discovered an unusual cause of suicide: country music! Steven Stack, from Wayne State University, Michigan, and James Gundlach, of Auburn University, Alabama, found that cities in which radio stations play an above-average amount of country music have higher-than-average suicide rates! Apparently, however, black people are immune to the effect.

Ecology

Was it because he used fizzy soft drinks that a Roman farmer was an 'agri-cola'?

Sales of Pepsi and Coke have shot up nearly 1,000% in an agricultural part of India where farmers are spraying the drinks on their crops to deal with insect pests! The farmers say that the sticky, sweet drinks attract ants which protect the crop by eating the larvae of insect pests. Their claims are, however, being refuted by Indian researchers who have since carried out tests on sample crops and 'not seen any increase in productivity, or eradication of pests'. It is not clear, though, whether they tested diet varieties too, which should be sufficient to put off even the most determined pests. Pepsi and Coke have meanwhile issued statements declaring that there is 'no scientific basis' for the practice!

Genetics

Forensic science

Illegal ivory trading still goes on – can't forensic science somehow trap the traders?

The worldwide ban on ivory trading was introduced in 1989 after elephant populations fell precipitously by 60 per cent from over 1.3 million in 1979 to around half a million by 1987. Despite the ban, however, conservationists estimate that 4,000 elephants, hippos and other ivory-bearing animals are still being killed every year to fuel the trade. Indeed, three of the world's largest ivory seizures have occurred in the last three years. (One culprit reponsible for boosting the illegal ivory trade recently is the Internet because individuals can buy and sell anonymously using facilities like eBay. Trades on the web are very hard to regulate because the word 'ivory' is commonly used in other ways – as in the expressions 'ivory soap' and 'ivory wedding dresses'.) Now a team at the University of Washington have come up with a powerful new tool to help in the battle against illegal poaching of ivory. Samuel Wasser and his team have constructed a genetic map of the elephants from 16 nations in Africa, enabling them to pinpoint the origins of a piece of ivory, with 80 per cent accuracy, to within a radius of 600 miles. They constructed the genetic database by isolating DNA from elephant dung and pieces of skin and then identified the genetic differences between elephant populations in different parts of the Africa to produce their overall map. DNA extracted from a piece of ivory can now be used to pinpoint where it came from, helping at least to identify poaching 'hot spots'.

Heredity
Histology

A mother passes on cells to her unborn baby. Is it possible for the baby to send cells back?

Scientists have known for some time that cells often jump across the placenta from a developing baby to enter the mother's bloodstream, but until recently the ultimate fate of these cellular trespassers remained a mystery. Now researchers at the New England Medical Center in Boston have discovered that these foetal cells can transform themselves into specialised cells in the thyroid, intestine, cervix, and gall bladder, and even help to heal injuries sustained by the skin. At the moment the team aren't clear what contribution, if any, these cells make to the healing process but an attractive hypothesis is that these foetal stem cells are helping to repair injuries sustained by the mother in what the researchers refer to as 'pay-back' for the price of pregnancy. But it's worth noting that a number of autoimmune diseases – conditions in which the immune system turns upon the body's healthy tissues – are much more common in women who have given birth, compared with women who have never been pregnant. It is possible that these autoimmune diseases, which include diabetes and thyroid disease, could occur *because* the trespassing foetal cells fool the immune system into attacking tissues that it shouldn't.

Ecology
Non-human biology

What do you do if you see an endangered animal eating an endangered plant?

That's what they're finding out in Mount Eccles National Park in Victoria, southern Australia. Victoria is home to the largest number of wild koalas of all the states in Australia. The total koala population in Australia plummeted from around 7 million at the time when Europeans first arrived in Australia in the late 1700s to a level of as few as 100,000 now. The current growth of the koala population is, however, putting too much strain on the eucalyptus trees which form their staple diet. The long-term preservation of the species depends as much upon the preservation of their habitat as upon the preservation of the animals itself, so conservationists plan to put 2,000 of the koalas on 'the pill' to slow down the population boom. According to Ian Walker, project manager, the method that has been chosen is a matchstick-sized hormone implant inserted under the skin between the shoulderblades. The implant, as used also by women all over the world, releases small amounts of female hormones to prevent pregnancy. The implants last about six years. The benefit of using this approach is that it is minimally invasive and completely reversible. Full fertility is restored once it is removed.

Factoid:
'The Eiffel Tower in Paris is 15 centimetres (6 inches) taller in mid-summer than it is in mid-winter.'
TRUE
Due to the expansion of metal when it's warm, the Eiffel Tower grows and shrinks by that much each year.

Hydrography
Marine ecology

Monitoring the oceans is important – but is it possible at all in the Arctic and Antarctic?

A team of oceanographers led by Mike Fedak from the Sea Mammal Research Unit at St Andrews University in Scotland have recruited a new breed of assistants to help them study remote polar waters – elephant seals. Traditionally, studies of the oceans, which can help in weather prediction and monitoring for climate change, are made by towing probes behind ships in order to measure salinity, depth and water movements. But researchers tend to be limited to studying areas where ships are going already, so some regions, such as the Antarctic, are more difficult to access than others. Mike Fedak and his team have solved the problem by producing a small fist-sized wearable probe and transmitter which can be attached to an elephant seal's head. These animals dive 40 times a day to depths ranging from 300 to 800 metres (1,000 to 1,800 feet) to hunt for fish and squid. As soon as a seal resurfaces, data collected by the probe during one of these dives is transmitted to a satellite overhead, which relays the data, together with the position of the animal, to the waiting oceanographers. The team initially tested the devices on two beluga whales off Norway before conducting a larger three-year trial which involved 70 elephant seals from four breeding areas around the Southern Ocean.

Food

Look – this is important: why is the quality of popcorn so variable?

US researchers have sussed out how science can solve the problem of unpopped corn, which is notorious for cracking teeth and dislodging fillings. By comparing the structure of good and bad 'popping' varieties, the scientists have pinned the problem down to the cellulose-rich outer shell of the corn, called the pericarp. The best popcorn comes from corn with the strongest pericarp – which works like a pressure-cooker, keeping the corn locked up tight until it reaches bursting point and explodes. They are now looking at ways to engineer the ideal pericarp into breeds of corn, and anticipate that they will have the perfect microwaveable variety on the market within a couple of years.

The senses
Sleep

Falling asleep while driving may be lethal. Isn't there any natural safety measure?

Yes, there would seem to be: a dose of peppermint or cinnamon. According to a study of stressed drivers, a squirt of the scent of either one of these flavours boosted alertness, decreased levels of frustration and anxiety, and lessened fatigue. Professor Bryan Raudenbush, author of the study, suggests that the agents serve as central nervous system stimulants. So everyone should now invest in a dangly peppermint or cinnamon air freshener for the car!

Medicine
Human biology

Brain injuries are time-consuming to diagnose – can anything speed the process up?

US researchers from Philadelphia's Drexel University have developed a hand-held monitoring device that can non-invasively pick up signs of bleeding into and around the brain, just using light. The hairbrush-sized hand-held clot-spotter uses a technique called functional near-infrared (fNIR) optical brain imaging and works by shining near-infrared light through the skull and underlying brain tissue. Collections of blood around the brain, or within the brain itself, cause the the light to be absorbed differently compared with normal tissue, flagging the area as a 'hot spot'. The information picked up by the probe is then transmitted wirelessly to a PDA or palmtop computer which maps out the head and highlights potential problem areas. In a pilot study involving 305 patients at Baylor College of Medicine, the device picked up 100% of bleeds around the brain (subdural and epidural haematomas) and 98% of bleeds into the brain, with no false positives. As a result it could make a significant contribution to the management of head-injured and stroke patients whose care is often delayed while doctors carry out a CT scan of the brain to determine the best course of action. Professor Kambiz Pourrezaei, one of the Drexel team, points out that it is also likely to solve the problem of finding head injuries in very young children brought to hospital following a fall. The device is now entering multicentre trials and is intended to be more widely available from early 2007.

Ecology

Biosphere

Plants get insects, birds and animals to pollinate them – how do *fish* come into it?

In an elegant study, researchers in the USA have shown how fish really can contribute to the pollination of flowers, highlighting the complex interdependence between totally different species. Robert Holt and his colleagues staked out four ponds, two with fish and two without, and counted the number of pollinating insects including bees and butterflies, the diversity and quality of the surrounding plant life, the number of dragonflies around the ponds, and the number of dragonfly larvae in the ponds. The team found large numbers of dragonfly larvae and mature dragonflies around those ponds that had no fish. These ponds also had the poorest surrounding plant growth and the fewest pollinating insects. But the ponds full of fish were surrounded by plant life that was much better pollinated, and showed a greater number of pollinating insects and far fewer dragonflies and dragonfly larvae. It turns out that dragonflies eat pollinating insects, but fish eat dragonfly larvae – so that more fish means fewer dragonflies, more pollinating insects, and happier plants. This study shows how human influences on one isolated aspect of an ecosystem – such as fishing – could have far-reaching consequences for many other animal and plant species.

Factoid:
'At the top of a mountain, the proportion of oxygen in the air is lower.'

FALSE
Air pressure is much lower, and there is less oxygen overall, but the *proportion* of the air that is oxygen is exactly the same – about 20%.

Life-support systems
Food
Communications

How did you know I was just about to go up to the bar to get another drink?

Thirsty researchers at the University of Munich, led by Andreas Butz, have developed a beer mat that automatically prompts bar staff for a refill when a glass is empty. The mat uses a pressure sensor to detect when the glass is getting low, and then signals the bar by radio for a top-up. The developers suggest that it could also be used as a bar-room voting device – for instance, in a karaoke setting, whereby drinkers quite literally raise their glasses to a good act. Unkind Germans, Australians and North Americans might alternatively suggest that for British beer-drinkers an electric heating element could also be installed to ensure that the beer is suitably warm upon serving.

Astronomy
Astro-geology

All right, so there really was water once on Mars – but did it run hot or cold?

Scientists have released a stunning sequence of images revealing recent (well, OK, within the last five million years) volcanic activity on our nearest celestial neighbour. Images relayed by *Mars Express* have revealed signs of glaciation and point to the possible existence of a frozen subsurface ocean harbouring who knows what.

Sound technology
The senses

Will the profoundly deaf ever be able to appreciate the profundities of punk rock?

Researchers at the National Physical Laboratory in Teddington, UK, have come up with a hearing aid that may help deaf people to appreciate music. Their device builds upon current cochlear-implant technology which uses electrodes to stimulate the nerves in the cochlea – the part of the ear which converts sounds into nerve signals the brain can understand and which is damaged in some forms of deafness. Current cochlear implants are very good for helping people to comprehend speech because they are specifically 'tuned' to the frequencies of speech. The new prototype, developed by Markys Cain and his colleagues, consists of a series of tiny bar-shaped elements coated with a piezo-electric material called polyvinylidene fluoride. By adjusting the length and shape of these elements they can be 'tuned' to vibrate at a much wider range of sound frequencies. The vibrations deform the piezo-electric coating, generating a tiny current which can be relayed to the auditory nerve as with a standard cochlear implant. The researchers believe that 10 to 20 of the resonating elements would be required to enable users to understand speech, and that only a few more could provide sufficient resolution to appreciate music. The prototype currently measures about 2 centimetres (four-fifths of an inch) square but the researchers are working on a miniature version capable of fitting inside the ear. Another major advantage of their approach is that unlike the present system, which requires an external power supply, the piezo-electric device can be entirely self-contained. The only downside is that the team anticipate that they are perhaps up to 10 years away from producing the device commercially.

Chemistry
Communications

Mobile phone screens or even CDs and DVDs can't be kept entirely scratch-free, can they?

Well, now there may be a way, thanks to the invention of a highly scratch-resistant coating developed over the last few years by the Japanese media-manufacturing giant TDK. The new polymer coating is so tough that a CD remains blemish-free even after being assaulted with wire wool and an arsenal of marker pens. Only a very determined attack with a Swiss army knife eventually succeeded in damaging the disk surface. The coating is applied in two layers. The first layer consists of tiny (50 micrometre) particles of silica (glass) embedded in a fluorine-containing resin. The silica provides strength while the fluorine repels water, preventing inks or paints from sticking to the surface. The top layer consists of a curing agent, called acetophenone, and another fluorine-containing resin. The mixture is 'set' by shining a quick blast of ultra-violet light onto it. The new material has also been welcomed by manufacturers Sony, Panasonic, and Philips who were planning to launch a successor to the DVD, called Blu-ray, in 2006. The new super-strength coating means there is no need to use 'caddy' or disk-holding systems with their new breed of disks, an important step forward since previous technologies that have used disk caddy systems have been marketing disasters!

Photography

Isn't it so frustrating to take pictures just too soon or just too late?

Have you ever waited ages for the perfect picture and then missed the moment because you were a fraction of a second too quick or too slow hitting the button? If this sounds like you, then Kodak may have the solution with an invention now added to their digital camera range, called BLILO – short for 'burst last in last out'. Once the BLILO button is pressed, the camera continuously shoots pictures at the rate of two a second, storing them on a separate 32-megabyte memory card. Once 30 pictures have been shot, the camera starts overwriting the old images with new ones, indefinitely. When the button is released, the last four frames taken – one of which hopefully contains the crucial moment – are transferred to the camera's main memory.

Safety

Vehicles

Visibility is essential for cyclists: but can it be increased still further?

Richard Hicks, a UK-based inventor, has come up with an ingenious way to make cyclists even more visible on roads at night: pedals that incorporate tiny dynamos to drive ultra-bright LEDs embedded in the front, rear and sides of the bike's pedals. The system charges up a supercapacitor, which stores charge and makes sure that the lights keep shining – and the cyclist remains visible – even when stopped at traffic lights and alongside other vehicles.

Medicine

Food

Why don't doctors diagnose disorders using a hand-held sensor like the one in *Star Trek*?

Raj Mutharasan, an engineer at Drexel University in Philadelphia, Pennsylvania, has developed a hand-held sensor that can pick up signs of food poisoning, such as *E. coli* contamination, in seconds. The device, which is as simple to use as a thermometer, uses the piezo-electric effect to weigh up how many microbes there are in a sample. It consists of a fine glass thread 5 millimetres (one-fifth of an inch) long and 1 millimetre (0.004 inch) thick which is coated with a piezo-electric ceramic called lead zirconate titanate (PZT). This layer is also peppered with antibodies which recognise the harmful O157 strain of *E. coli*. When an alternating electric current is applied, it causes the PZT coating to expand and contract, causing the glass thread to vibrate at a certain frequency, which can be measured. But when the antibodies lock onto *E. coli*, the weight of the bacteria alters the vibrations of the glass; the more bacteria there are, the greater the change in the vibration frequency. The sensor works in liquid extracted from the food being examined, and tests so far show that it can detect as few as 4 bacterial cells in one millilitre of liquid. It can also pick up other pathogens, including *Listeria*, and various agencies are now teaming up with the Drexel researchers to explore its potential in the detection of bio-terror weapons such as anthrax.

Genetics

Non-human biology

But think for a moment – if snails can fly, why not pigs?

In his famous book *On the Origin of Species*, Charles Darwin pointed out 150 years ago that there are many remote islands on Earth populated by snails that seem to be very similar to snails found elsewhere. Yet snails can't swim and their eggs are destroyed by sea water – so how did they get there? Darwin speculated that snails might be stowing away aboard migrating birds, but how has remained a mystery ever since. Now, though, a team of researchers led by Cambridge snail expert Richard Preece has used the science of genetics to prove that Darwin was almost certainly right. The researchers genetically fingerprinted a species of European *Balea* snails and compared them with similar snails found 9,000 kilometres (5,500 miles) away on the remote Tristan de Cunha Islands in the South Atlantic. The genetic sequences are almost identical. But the snails couldn't have travelled there by boat since the islands were first populated only 500 years ago and the snails' DNA 'clock' – a measure of the differences between their DNA and that of their European counterparts – suggests that they have been on the islands for much longer than that. Nor are similar snails found on any other landmasses near by. So, the researchers conclude, the only way they could have made their journey was by air – exactly as Darwin thought. In fact these snails create a particularly sticky mucus which enables them to glue themselves tightly to birds' feet and feathers, making the theory much more likely.

Domestic events
Human biology

Oh, these shirts are filthy! Why can't someone invent a fabric that just stays clean?

Housewives (and house-husbands) may soon have emptier laundry baskets and lower water bills to look forward to, thanks to researchers at Clemson University, who have discovered how to make a dirt-resistant fabric coating. The new highly water-repellent coating is made from a polymer gel (polyglycidyl methacrylate) mixed with silver nanoparticles and promises to offer superior resistance to dirt, which means that it needs cleaning much less often. Treated clothes can be made in any colour because the coating is added after the material has been dyed. Phil Brown, one of the researchers behind the new coating, likens the concept to a lotus plant, the leaves of which are known to 'self-clean' by repelling dirt and water. When water does come along, any dirt present is carried away much more easily. In the same way, dirt can simply be sprayed or wiped from clothes made with the new coating which, unlike conventional water-repellent coatings, is permanently bonded to the fabric so it can't wash off. The team is now working on a way to engineer antimicrobial particles into the coating, which would also help to cut down on odours such as cigarette smoke. It might even help to nullify body odours (so a wearer would presumably not need to wash either!).

Factoid:
'The acid in most car batteries is hydrochloric acid.'
FALSE
It is sulphuric acid.

The senses
Human biology

Dogs are brilliant at following a scent. Why can't humans do that?

Scientists in India may have proved that it is not just our ears that work in stereo – our noses do too. Raghav Rajan and his colleagues have found that in just one sniff (lasting about a tenth of a second), and despite having nostrils only 3 millimetres (an eighth of an inch) apart, rats can tell which direction a smell is coming from. The researchers piped in smells which were presented from either the left or right and trained the animals to lick one of two water spouts according to where they thought a smell was coming from. The rats were correct 80% of the time, but when the researchers temporarily blocked one of their nostrils, the animals' performances dropped considerably. To find out how the rats were doing this, the researchers next recorded the electrical activity in the parts of the rat brain responsible for processing smells. They found populations of nerve cells that responded selectively to the direction from which smells arrive. These cells essentially compare the smell signals coming into both nostrils; whichever cells switch on first then switch off their counterparts on the other side of the brain, enabling the animal to pinpoint the origin of a smell. Because the human olfactory system is wired up in a similar way, it is likely that the same thing is true for us ... and that TV adverts and comic strips showing kids following their noses to find a feast are not just fantasy after all.

Drug and solvent abuse

Are you quite sure that is what is meant by 'The river is high today'?

Researchers in Italy have published the world's first report tracking cocaine use in Italian cities through an analysis of the local river water. Ettore Zuccato and colleagues from Milan's Mario Negri Institute for Pharmacological Research tested water samples from the River Po and water-treatment plants serving several medium-sized cities and found that at least (US)$400,000 worth of excreted (i.e. used) cocaine was flowing along the river each day! The findings suggest that the existing estimates of cocaine use – roughly 15,000 doses daily – are significantly short of the mark, and that more realistically at least 40,000 doses are being consumed in the region every day.

Communications

The mind

Does the content of a TV programme affect how viewers heed the adverts?

It would seem to. Over 300 student volunteers took part in a study run by psychologists at the University of Michigan, which involved watching a range of TV programmes before taking a memory test. Watching shows containing a sexual content caused the volunteers to be 21% less likely to remember the adverts, whereas violent scenes, including wrestling, made viewers 17% less likely to recall brands. This result has obvious implications for sponsors and advertisers ...

Weather
Diseases and disorders

Does long-range weather forecasting help anyone other than tourists and ark-builders?

Yes – some serious endemic diseases are climate-linked, and advance warning of particular forms of weather can greatly assist the mobilisation of resources to counter them. The UK's Tim Palmer and his team have used an ensemble of climate models to come up with an early-warning system for malaria in parts of Africa. The incidence of malaria is strongly linked to climate, wetter years resulting in more widespread outbreaks of the disease. But by the time it is determined whether a year is 'wet' or 'dry', it has until now been too late to move resources to where they are most needed to treat sufferers, or to control the mosquitoes that spread the disease. The new weather-forecasting model, however, can predict the scale of the rainy season up to four months ahead of time, so enabling infection-control teams and antimalarial measures to be deployed in high-risk areas well in advance. To come up with their new model, the researchers combined the forecasts of three different climate-predicting systems and then compared weather and malaria case records from the past 20 years with their own predictions for the same period. Basing their work on specific regions of Botswana they were able to show that the system made highly accurate retrospective predictions. In the light of 500 million cases of malaria occurring worldwide each year, this finding potentially adds a powerful new weapon to our antimalarial arsenal.

Petrol engines
Ecology

Isn't there an alternative to using the choke to help start a cold engine?

Engineers at Colorado State University have come up with a clever way to make cars start more easily on cold days, and reduce the amount of unburnt particulate matter produced by a cold engine. At start-up a pump sucks out the volatile vapour hovering above the fuel in the tank and squirts it into the engine in place of the regular fuel. Being more volatile, the vapour burns more readily, so the engine starts more easily and runs more cleanly. Once things warm up, the pump shuts down and the engine returns to getting its fuel the normal way.

Domestic events
Light

Why do wineglasses, if washed often, lose transparency and go 'foggy'?

Researchers at Lehigh-Unilever have found out why some glasses develop a white discoloration with age and use that won't go away no matter how well you wash them. It's not down to dirty living habits but to tiny imperfections present in the glass when it was made. With repeated cleaning in the dishwasher, these tiny cracks open up making light that shines on the glass bounce about rather than travelling straight through. For exactly the same reason, snow looks white whereas water is transparent.

Palaeontology

Yes, but what kind of dinosaur was it that evolved into *Tyrannosaurus rex*?

Researchers in China have discovered the earliest known relative of *Tyrannosaurus rex*, filling in a big piece of the puzzle over where these 'tyrant dinosaurs' came from. Xing Xu of the Palaeontological Institute of Beijing and his international colleagues have described a pair of fossils dating back 160 million years that were uncovered in an area of northwest China in 2003. Tyrannosaur specimens found up till now have all been roughly 65 million years old: although researchers were able to trace their history back to 120 million years or so, previous considerable anatomical adaptations had obscured any evidence of their origins beyond that. But now this new find – named *Guanlong wucaii* ('crowned dragon of the five-coloured rocks') – is a small 3-metre (10-foot) beast which combines many of the features characteristic of its more 'modern' descendants including U-shaped teeth and fused nasal bones, with many more primitive traits including long arms, a three-fingered hand, blade-like teeth in the sides of the jaw and a primitive pelvis. Also unlike the later tyrannosauroids, it had a small crest running from its snout to the back of its neck (which is why in its scientific name it is described as 'crowned'). This missing link means that researchers can write up more of where we now believe tyrannosaurs came from, and also designates them as close relatives of modern-day birds which are descended from the same ancestor.

Medicine
Ultrasound technology

Is it true that in some A&E patients it is difficult to locate a vein for a blood infusion?

Yes it is – particularly if the accident or emergency has injured a baby, a very fat person, or a person who is seriously dehydrated. But help is now at hand. Researchers at the Georgia Institute of Technology have developed a lightweight, portable ultrasound device to help doctors find blood vessels quickly, potentially saving precious minutes in an emergency. Their instrument – imaginatively named a 'vein finder' – consists of a disposable probe and needle guide linked to a box containing the electronics. The user slides the probe over the skin surface and an alarm is triggered when it locates a vein. A needle is then fed through the guide which is positioned at just the right angle to ensure that the needle slides into the vein. The probe emits a thin beam of ultrasound about the width of a pencil lead which is reflected by the tissue and back into the probe. Because blood moves around the body, the ultrasound frequencies reflected from a blood vessel are different from the frequencies bounced back from stationary tissue, enabling the device to pinpoint vessels with great accuracy. But the frequencies also reveal the direction in which the blood is moving, so additionally distinguishing between veins and arteries (because the blood they contain flows in opposite directions). So far the machine has proved highly effective in tests on laboratory tissue designed to model a human arm, and the team is now adapting it for human trials. The researchers point out that it could make a huge difference to obtaining rapid intravenous access not only in very young A&E patients (in whom veins are notoriously difficult to locate) but in patients who have suffered a recent traumatic cardiac arrest.

Computer technology
Communications

I've heard of the 'speaking clock', but what's this about a speaking bottle?

Most people get chatty when they've had a few, but they may be competing with the wine itself when a new Italian talking wine bottle hits the shelves sometime soon. Tuscan company Modulgraf have come up with a way to embed a chip inside the wine bottle label which can then be programmed with all the patter you would normally receive only from an experienced oenologist (wine expert). The idea is that next time you pop to the drink shop you can browse around the shop using a cigarette-packet-sized audio device to listen to each bottle extolling its virtues. It could also help to prevent counterfeiting. A number of wine-makers had already expressed keen interest in the product by the end of 2005.

Factoid:
'A kettle full of hot (but not necessarily boiling) water weighs exactly the same as the same kettle containing the same amount of cold water.'

FALSE
Einstein's famous equation $E = mc^2$ stands for energy = mass [or weight] x the speed of light, squared. Since the speed of light is a constant, if the energy, or temperature, of the water in the kettle goes up, then so must the weight, to keep the equation balanced.

Food

The mind

Hypnosis involves the power of suggestion – but how suggestible are people anyway?

US researchers from the University of Washington and the University of California have found that they can fool people into avoiding certain foods by falsely telling them that they had a bad experience with the food as a child. Daniel Bernstein and his colleagues recruited a group of students and quizzed them about their dietary habits before returning some 'individual computer-generated feedback' to each of them. The feedback – which was actually identical for all of them – said that they had been made ill by strawberry ice cream when they were little. When the group were later followed up and quizzed again, up to 40% of them subsequently claimed that strawberry ice cream really had made them ill when they were very young, and that their inclination to eat strawberry ice cream had now distinctly lessened. Although the researchers were unable to achieve the same results with French fries or chocolate ice cream, they suggest that their approach might help to prevent people, especially children, from eating unhealthily and carrying their bad eating habits into adulthood.

Medicine
Human biology

Bacteria assist in digestion – but how come our immune system lets them?

Scientists have worked out how we manage to carry around trillions of bacteria in our guts without causing our immune system to go into meltdown. The bugs give themselves a sugary coating to disguise themselves as human gut cells.

Astronomy

The Earth gets meteor showers. Presumably the other planets do too?

Analysing data sent back by the NASA Mars rover *Spirit*, researchers noticed a large streak across one of the images of the Martian sky. The timing of the photograph coincided closely (in March 2004) with the visit of a comet called Wiseman-Skiff and its attendant cloud of meteors. One of these meteors probably grazed past Mars at a leisurely 11 kilometres per second (7 miles per second), briefly lighting up the sky. The images suggest that *Spirit* inadvertently captured on camera astronomers' first glimpse of a shooting star as seen from Mars. The findings are important because analysis of these events can provide information about the chemical events that take place when a meteor meets an atmosphere rich in carbon dioxide, just like that of the early Earth.

Non-human biology

Can't you remember *anything,* you birdbrain?

Actually, UK and Canadian researchers have shown that hummingbirds have an impressive memory for times and places. Because they burn up calories so quickly, hummingbirds cannot afford to waste time and energy making repeat visits to flowers from which they have already collected nectar – at least, not until the flower has had time to replenish its sugar stores. As a result, these birds have evolved to memorise the locations and times of the flowers they have visited ... and they can time their return journeys to within minutes of the flowers' replenishing their nectar supplies. To show that this was the case, Edinburgh University's Susan Healy and her colleagues set up an array of eight fake flowers, each containing sugar solution, within the territories of free-living hummingbirds in the Canadian Rockies. Some of the flowers were refilled with sugar every 10 minutes, whereas others were refilled every 20 minutes. The researchers monitored how often the birds visited each of the flowers. Incredibly, they appeared to be able to keep eight mental stopwatches running simultaneously, because they quickly learned to return to the 10-minute refill flowers after 10 minutes, and the 20-minute refill flowers after 20 minutes, and knew exactly which flowers they had visited at what time, and in what order! This was maintained throughout the course of a day. Although scientists were aware that hummingbirds had a good memory for places, no one had appreciated quite how good they are at keeping separate times and durations!

The senses
Human biology

And just whose savage breast are you hoping to soothe with that electric nose-flute?

Researchers from Italy and the University of Oxford have found that your choice in music can affect your stress levels. Peter Sleight and Luciano Bernadi played short excerpts from a range of musical genres including raga, Beethoven, rap, techno and Vivaldi, to 24 male and female volunteers, half of whom were musicians, half of whom were not. They found that the faster the music, and the more complex the rhythms, the greater the level of arousal amongst the subjects, which they assessed by recording heart rate and breathing. Conversely, more meditative, soothing tempos produce the opposite effect, the raga (Indian classical music) producing the most pronouncedly calming effects. Overall the effects were most marked amongst the musicians, probably because they are trained to listen for a regular rhythm or beat in the music, which they may then synchronise their breathing rate with, but all of the subjects responded, leading the researchers to suggest that music therapy could be useful in the management of heart disease and strokes. The reverse implication is that people who listen all the time to fast music with complex rhythms may in fact be causing themselves unnecessary stress.

Sociology
Education

How can you learn when you can't see the information clearly?

A simple $20 solar-powered invention is making a world of difference to education in Africa. Because in many African countries people have to work for a living during the day, the only education some people can get takes place at night. But until now in remote villages without electricity, classes of 40 students have had to squeeze together around one or two kerosene lamps, sometimes even having to take turns in seeing the words and pictures that mean so much. As a result, key messages about nutrition and HIV awareness have not been passed on, and for many learners even basic general literacy has been impossible to achieve. Now, though, the Kinkajou Projector (named after the saucer-eyed South American mammal renowned for its prodigious night-time vision) looks set to change all that. This simple device comprises a super-bright LED light shone through a micro-film capable of holding 10,000 slide images. The slides are projected onto a screen or flat surface at a size suitable for class visibility. The LED bulbs last for 100,000 hours each and are far more robust than standard power-hungry incandescent projector lamps: they run from a 12-volt solar-recharged battery. With one of these projectors a whole class can see and learn far more effectively.

Factoid:
'The sea is becoming more salty all the time.'

FALSE
The sea's 3% salt content has remained static for millions of years because it naturally and constantly loses as much salt as it gains.

Medicine
Diseases and disorders

Gold salts are used in heart treatment, but does gold have other medical uses?

Researchers at the Georgia Institute of Technology have found that tiny filaments of gold (measured in nanometres, or millionths of a millimetre) can be used to home in on, and destroy, tumour cells buried deep in tissues. Mostafa and Ivan El-Sayed had shown previously that small spherical gold particles could be coated with antibodies to make them bind to a cell surface marker called epidermal growth factor receptor (EGFR), which is frequently found on the surfaces of cancer cells but is absent from the surfaces of healthy cells. These gold particles made it very easy to spot the cancer cells they had locked onto because they glowed when laser light of a certain frequency was shone on them. But visible light does not penetrate more than a few millimetres into tissue, and most cancers occur well beneath the surface, limiting the benefit of the gold method. By stretching the nanospheres into a 20-nanometre by 60-nanometre rod, however, the researchers found that they would respond to laser light at longer near-infrared (NIR) wavelengths which can pass harmlessly through healthy tissue to reach a tumour. Within a cancer the nanorods boost the absorption of the laser light, quite literally cooking the tumour cells. The El-Sayeds describe how an initial test using healthy and cancerous cells from the mouth showed that cancer cells coated with the gold nanorods could be destroyed using only half the dose of laser energy usually required to kill a cell.

Palaeontology
Ecology

If global warming goes on, won't quite a few animals become endangered species?

Indeed they will. Most wild animals, after all, rely on a natural habitat based on a specific climate with regular seasons. But some creatures will be affected worse than others. If the present trend in global warming continues, reindeer populations, for example, could well face severe stress, disappearing from large portions of their current range – that is, if the predictions of palaeontologists and archaeologists from France and America turn out to be true. Françoise Delpech and Donald Grayson have been studying reindeer bones unearthed in a cave in the Dordogne region that was once home to Neanderthal Man. They have followed an archaeological sequence in the cave (by which the deeper you go the older things are), dating from 12,000 to over 65,000 years ago, to work out how the population of reindeer have varied with the summertime climate data for the region, which is known from pollen records from the same time period. They found that as summertime temperatures went up, the number of reindeer went down, and when things really warmed up, about 10,000 years ago, the reindeer disappeared completely. 'Reindeer just cannot tolerate high summer temperatures,' Donald Grayson says. 'They have almost no sweat glands, and keep their insulation – a heavy pelt – in summer.' So it looks as if Santa could well be searching for a replacement for Rudolph in 100 years or so. Let's hope he goes for an environmentally-friendly alternative.

Plant biology
Ecology

Plants use many protective mechanisms. What's the most outlandish?

One of the most extraordinary is to get carnivorous mites to act as private bodyguards. Dutch and Israeli scientists have described how they pursuaded cress plants – which are used as models for plant research – to produce a class of chemicals that can recruit armies of mites to flock to the plant and devour any pests that try to make a meal of their new 'charge'. To achieve this feat the researchers borrowed a strawberry gene which, when added to the cress plants, enabled the cress plants to begin producing two new bodyguard-marshalling compounds called terpenoids. These substances are strongly attractive to predatory mites but are very difficult to produce artificially. It has been suggested that a similar technique could be used to protect common field crops without needing to resort to potentially toxic insecticide sprays.

Ecology
Human biology

Might it really be better for the environment if we were all vegetarians?

Consultant physicist Alan Calverd has calculated that rearing the animals we eat accounts for over 20% of the anthropogenic (man-made) carbon dioxide that is released into the atmosphere each year. Leaving meat off the dinner plate could therefore help to slash greenhouse emissions ... and, according to Calverd, might even make the world population healthier.

Drugs and drug abuse

Your thinking's gone to pot – why shouldn't I turn you out to grass?

Despite the fact that marijuana now has an image as a safe drug, enjoying a decriminalised status in many countries, scientists have announced that it can produce long-term changes in the brain's bloodflow, and that the changes may still be present even after a month of not smoking. Ronald Herning and Jean Luc Cadet from the National Institute on Drug Abuse in Baltimore used non-invasive ultrasound tests to measure the flow of blood through the brains of 54 marijuana-users and 18 non-using controls. The researchers found that blood flowed much more quickly through the brains of the marijuana smokers, and that their vessels had a greater overall resistance to blood flow, compared with non-users. The changes were similar to (but greater than) those often seen in the brains of the elderly or of patients with chronic high blood pressure or long-term diabetes, suggesting that they are caused by the narrowing of small blood vessels. But are the changes permanent? The researchers found that light to moderate marijuana-users after a month of abstinence did show an improvement in their brain bloodflow, but amongst previously heavy users (more than 70 joints per week) the changes were irreversible, indicating that marijuana use may cause permanent abnormalities in the small blood vessels of the brain.

Human biology
Domestic events

Mirror, O Mirror, I ask you in rhyme – What will I look like in five years' time?

With features like yours, is it wise to ask even something as dumb as a mirror? Still, a system under development in France supposedly makes it possible to predict how you will look in five years' time, based upon your present lifestyle. To begin, the computer takes a picture of you. It then builds up a profile of your behaviour by watching you at home using a network of webcams which pick up couch-potato tendencies including clandestine trips to the fridge for junk food or beer. The system also periodically enquires what you are eating or drinking. Once your profile is complete, the computer then calculates how this lifestyle will reflect on your appearance over five years. Too many snacks? It will add an extra chin or two. Too much alcohol? Prepare for wrinkles, a red nose and blotchy skin. Accenture Technology, who are developing the system, intend to go on to produce a real-time system capable of providing users with a genuine sense of looking into the future to see how their present lifestyle is going to affect them, which, they say, might help motivate over-indulgers to make some changes!

Factoid:
'The world's biggest slug can weigh up to 15 kilo–grams (more than 30 pounds; over 2 stone).'
TRUE
The Californian sea hare is a slug-like mollusc that lives underwater in kelp forests. It can grow up to 1 metre (39 inches) long.

Medicine
Diseases and disorders

Classically, cancer spreads from one body site to another – but do we know how?

For a long time we thought we knew. But Rosandra Kaplan and her colleagues from the Sloan-Kettering Cancer Center in New York have added an important piece to the jigsaw puzzle of how cancers spread to other parts of the body – a process known as metastasis. Indeed, it is usually the spread to remote sites, rather than the original (primary) tumour itself, that causes the majority of cancer deaths, so tracking down how this process occurs is an important landmark in the search for effective anti-cancer therapies. For many years researchers thought that cells merely peeled away from a cancer and travelled via the bloodstream to other tissues, where they seeded fresh tumours. But it turns out that that is not the whole story. Instead, cancers send an emissary first, in the form of bone marrow cells. Kaplan and her team worked with mice that had been engineered to produce glowing green bone marrow cells. When tumour cells (engineered to glow red) were injected into the mice the researchers first saw green (bone marrow) cells appear in the lungs and only after this happened did the red tumour cells take up residence, in the same place. The researchers suggest that cancers produce a substance that mobilises bone marrow cells and enables them to dock in certain tissues that the cancer likes to invade. Once the marrow cells have then prepared the ground at the new site, tumour cells can move in. The team have now identified a cell marker rather like a molecular grappling hook that the tumour cells use to cling on to the bone marrow cells. When this cellular marker was blocked chemically, no tumour spread occurred, suggesting that the same trick might work in humans with early-stage (pre-metastatic) cancers.

Sleep
Human biology

Haven't I always said that you needed your beauty sleep?

Scientists from the University of Bristol have found that obesity might be linked to not getting enough sleep. Dr Shahrad Taheri and colleagues looked at the levels of two key appetite-regulating hormones called leptin and ghrelin collected from 1,000 normal volunteers. Leptin makes people feel full, whereas ghrelin makes people feel hungry. The researchers found that subjects who reported habitually sleeping for only five hours a night had 15% more appetite-boosting ghrelin, and 15% less appetite-suppressing leptin, in their bloodstreams compared with people who slept for eight hours. The researchers argue that these appetite-stimulating hormonal changes probably make poor sleepers more likely to indulge in 'midnight feasts' and other food foraging behaviours that ultimately lead to over-eating and weight gain. Indeed, the light-sleepers in the study were statistically more likely to be heavier. Over the last 50 years the average person has reduced the amount of sleep that he or she gets per night by about two hours, which might therefore be contributing to the present obesity epidemic. Good sleep, together with other lifestyle measures, may be an important way to reverse the present trend.

Human biology

Her eyes might follow you around the room – but does she *like you*?

According to research from the University of Amsterdam, the Mona Lisa (Leonardo's *La Gioconda*) is 83% happy, 9% disgusted, 6% fearful and 2% angry. That's the interpretation of Nicu Sebe's emotion-recognition software which he is developing in collaboration with US scientists at the University of Illinois. Their algorithm examines key facial features, including the curvature of the lips and wrinkles around the eyes, to assign a score under six different emotional categories. Sebe used a database of 'neutral' young female faces against which to compare the expression of the Mona Lisa. The researchers are aiming to develop emotion-recognition systems to build computers that are sensitive to human moods.

Vehicles

Did I notice *what* scratch on the car when you brought it back?

Japanese car giant Nissan are set to launch the perfect product for careless drivers – a paint that automatically repairs minor scrapes and scratches. The paint contains a highly elastic resin that forms a protective coat over the paint. If the paintwork is dented, but no paint is removed, heat from the sun melts the resin which flows back into shape, returning the surface to its original smoothness.

Diseases and disorders
Medicine

Yes, but surely breathing healthy seaside air is renowned as being good for people?

Ah, but this is more than merely 'healthy seaside air', and the people involved are not themselves in a healthy condition. Researchers in Australia and the USA have stumbled upon an extremely cheap yet highly effective way to help sufferers of the lung condition cystic fibrosis to breathe more easily – a dose of salt water. Scientists at the University of North Carolina and the University of Sydney compared the lung function of almost 200 cystic fibrosis patients given either a saline solution twice as salty as the sea to breathe in, or a placebo solution. They found that the patients given the strong salt solution showed significant improvements in lung function and day-to-day quality of life. The effect seems to occur because the strong salt solution pulls water from the airway tissue onto the airway surfaces, making it much easier to shift the sticky mucus that accumulates in the lungs of cystic fibrosis sufferers. The University of Carolina's Scott Donaldson, one of the doctors behind the study, said 'We're very excited that this simple and inexpensive therapy turned out to be so effective and well-tolerated in patients with cystic fibrosis. It gives us great hope that the use of this therapy will reduce how often patients feel ill, will slow the decline of lung function, and will help these people live longer.'

Food

What do you mean 'This meat is off'? Off what?

Off the back of an unmarked van in a sidestreet, perhaps. UK researchers based at the University of Manchester have developed a technology that can identify contaminated meat in seconds, just by shining a light on it. At the moment, by the time a dodgy batch of meat is detected it could already be on the supermarket shelves or, worse still, in the stomachs of the unaware. But unlike existing techniques, which look for the bugs themselves, the new approach developed by David Ellis uses infrared light to pick up the biochemical signatures of bacterial activity. As the number of bugs rises, so does the amount of waste they produce – and that is what the infrared beam can detect. So far the technique has been shown to work effectively for chicken and beef, but there is no reason it shouldn't work for other foodstuffs too.

Communications

Isn't this what they call the shortest distance between two points?

A Florida-based inventor has come up with an idea for a 'stiff rope' to get round the problem of trying to hold out a line to someone from a boat or when climbing a rockface. David Chroman's rope has a hollow plastic tube embedded down the middle of the strand. Blowing air into the tube from a compressed air supply causes the rope to stiffen and become sufficiently rigid to support itself when held out from a boat, making it easily 'grabbable'.

Human biology
Games

OK, my index finger is short. But do you think that means I can't smash your teeth in?

Canadian psychologists from the University of Alberta have found that the length of a man's index finger, relative to the ring finger, can be used to predict how inclined he is to be physically aggressive. Dr Peter Hurd and his team surveyed 300 undergraduates and found that the shorter the index finger compared with the fourth (ring) finger, the more physically (but apparently not verbally) aggressive the individual tends to be throughout life. The relative lengths of the fingers depend upon how much testosterone the developing baby is exposed to in the womb: higher testosterone exposure produces a longer ring finger, and a more aggressive male. On the other hand – er, sorry about that – men with less 'masculine' finger lengths seem to be more prone to depression. But neither of these findings apply to women. Yet the results of the survey fit with other studies, including those of Dr John Manning who measured the finger lengths of over 300 footballers and found that those with the longer fingers tended to be superior in their abilities. The same applies to other sports including judo, squash, track athletics and rugby. The Alberta team is now looking at the lengths of ice hockey players' fingers to find out whether longer fingers are associated with more aggressive play (and hence more penalties)!

Plant biology
Ecology

Are *Acers* so called because they have an ace up their leaves?

Why do trees turn a pretty colour in autumn? Usually, it's due to the breakdown of chlorophyll, the green pigment that helps plants to turn sunlight into chemical energy. As the chlorophyll disappears, other vibrant colours within the leaf – including red- and golden-coloured molecules called carotenoids – are revealed. But for some trees, including maples (*Acer* species), the colour change might signal more sinister intentions. In these plants the leaves turn a beautiful scarlet colour because an additional class of molecules, called anthocyanins, are actively manufactured within the leaf just before it is dropped from the tree. Trees cannot afford to waste energy on a process that is not beneficial to them, so the colour change must serve some useful purpose. To find out what it might be, researchers Frank Frey and Maggie Eldridge from Colgate University in the USA prepared leaf extracts from maples and added them to some lettuce seedlings. The lettuce plants all promptly died, leading the researchers to suggest that when maple trees drop their leaves, the anthocyanins leach into the soil, poisoning any other plants which might threaten to compete with the maple's own seedlings the following spring. The theory seems plausible because anthocyanins are chemically very similar to a substance called catechin, which is known to poison plant roots.

Diseases and disorders

HIV derives from monkeys – could Ebola likewise stem from animal viruses?

Eric Leroy and his colleagues of the CIRMF, Gabon, have solved a 30-year puzzle about the lethal Ebola virus – where it comes from, and where it goes when it is not causing outbreaks amongst humans and primates. To track down Ebola's 'natural' host, the researchers set traps to catch all of the small animals that they could close to sites of Ebola outbreaks in Gabon. In all they collected over 1,000 specimens which they then analysed for signs of the virus. The tests showed that three species of fruit bats were positive. The researchers suspect that the virus could be finding its way into humans when hungry locals capture and eat infected bats, and are urging people to avoid the practice.

Non-human biology

Is it true that giant tortoises make genial companions?

Game wardens in Kenya rescued Owen, the one-year-old baby hippo, after they found him suffering from dehydration and separated from his herd. They temporarily put him into an enclosure in Haller Park with a 120-year-old giant tortoise called Mzee (Swahili for 'old man') and, says Sabine Baer, one of the senior park employees, 'he immediately lumbered over to the tortoise which has a dark grey colour similar to grown hippos.' The two have since become inseparable.

The senses

The music goes round and round ... and comes out *where?*

Frustrating, isn't it, having a tune go round in your head that you just can't seem to shake off ? Scientists from Scotland and the USA have now pinpointed the part of the brain responsible for the so-called 'ear worms' or such 'auditory images' by watching a brain-scanner as volunteers experienced them. The researchers played the subjects excerpts of well-known songs with short (2- to 5-second) silent gaps in them. As a control they also played them songs they had never heard before, also containing gaps. The volunteers reported that in the well-known songs, even though the music had stopped, they could still 'hear' the song continuing inside their heads. So the areas of the brain that lit up on the brain-scanner at these times must have been the ones responsible for filling in the gaps. The researchers found that a region of the brain's temporal lobe called the auditory association area, which is located above the ear and is essentially where sounds are decoded and linked to meaningful information, became much more active during silent gaps in well-known songs. There was also a difference between songs that were instrumentals and those that contained lyrics: the instrumentals required a much greater amount of grey matter to reconstruct, presumably because the lyrics provide a shortcut for the retrieval of the information.

Geology

Victorian adventure and detective authors loved quicksand. It does exist, doesn't it?

What is quicksand, how does it work, and are you likely to sink into it without trace? Moreover, what is the best way to escape if you do find yourself stuck in it? These were the questions bothering Dutch researcher Daniel Bonn when he recently wandered around some Iranian quicksand pits which, local legend has it, have been known to swallow camels from time to time, and for that matter anyone who cared to disagree with the local regime. To solve the riddle he recreated some Iranian quicksand in his lab and used the resulting model to figure out how quicksand works. He discovered, to his surprise, that it is actually impossible to drown in it (as long as you don't do something stupid) – indeed, you should only sink to waist depth. But do not try to pull a stuck person out, because the force required to extricate just a stuck foot is similar to that needed to move a medium-sized car, so you might inadvertently pull the person apart! It would seem that any part of the body kept moving horizontally will stay within a watery level, but any part of the body left vertical and stationary will at once be surrounded by clogging and heavy quicksand much too heavy to pull straight upwards through. So the best way to escape is to turn a stuck body part in small circles to resuspend the sand particles in water, withdrawing gently and gradually as you do so. Try to float, in fact, being careful not to be too energetic about it.

Sociology
Domestic events

Yeah – there's this apple on this tree. Looks delicious. Take a bite, eh, Adam?

A study carried out by researchers at the University of St Andrews, Scotland, has shown that what women look for in a man has changed dramatically in recent years. Fhionna Moore and her colleagues surveyed 1,851 women between the ages of 18 and 35 and found that whereas in the past women had been attracted largely by the size of mens' wallets and their consequent capability of maintaining their wives through their childbearing years, the woman of today values looks over riches. That said, younger, more ambitious, cash-strapped females in the study still rated a man's means over his looks – provided he was young too. Commenting on the study, Moore points out that economic constraints on women are not as strong as they were 50 years ago. 'It is this change, in comparison to historical constraints, that I believe influences mate preferences.' So it looks as if metrosexual man – complete with moisturiser – is here to stay, then.

Factoid:
'All mammals are warm-blooded: it's one reason they are mammals, not reptiles.'

FALSE
The naked mole-rat is nature's only example of a genuinely cold-blooded mammal, but various others (like the hyrax or *dassie* of South Africa) rely on some time in full sunlight every day to be fully active.

The mind
Human biology

For some people, hoarding things can be a sort of compulsion, can't it?

Some people take hoarding to extremes – and for some of them, yes, there would seem to be a compulsive element, although little study has been carried out. But now scientists have pinpointed the part of the brain that makes people and animals want to collect things. Over 70 different animal species, including humans, show hoarding behaviour – which mostly involves stashing away food – but till a couple of years ago no one knew where the drive to collect (whether stamps, pencils, or even Dr Who videos) was based. Brain researchers Roy and Lucille Carver, from the University of Iowa, cracked the problem by studying the brain scans of a number of human patients who had developed unusual hoarding tendencies – to the extent that they would fill their houses with useless rubbish such as broken fridges, toasters, or junk mail. Although the items were useless to the patients, who otherwise showed normal brain function in terms of intellect and memory, the hoarders strongly resisted any notion of getting rid of the stuff. The researchers found that the patients with this hoarding behaviour all had small areas of damage to a particular part of the right side of the brain known as the mesial prefrontal cortex. Now that they have pinpointed the region of the brain which drives collecting behaviour, scientists hope that it will provide clues to tackling the problem when it crops up in other conditions including Tourette's, obsessive compulsive disorder, certain dementias, and schizophrenia.

Medicine
Drink

Who *needs* an excuse to have a glass of red wine?

Scientists have found that resveratrol – a well-known anti-oxidant in red wine – as well as helping to prevent arterial disease, can limit the progress of another condition known as cardiac fibrosis. When the heart is overworked by high blood pressure or heart failure, cells in the heart known as fibro-blasts go into overdrive and produce an excessive amount of the fibrous tissue collagen. The accumulation of collagen makes the cardiac muscle so much stiffer that it cannot pump efficiently. But US researchers have shown that resveratrol blocks the action of a key hormone known as angiotensin II, which is responsible for causing the production of excess collagen in the heart in the first place. Using cells taken from the hearts of rats, the scientists found that pre-treating the cultured cells with resveratrol before adding the angiotensin II hormone prevented the fibroblasts in the culture from making excessive collagen, suggesting that the chemical might have anti-fibrotic properties when taken in moderation. Studies have shown that most dark (red) wines contain resveratrol – part of the vine plant's natural defences against disease – although amounts do vary between different varie-ties of grape and the resveratrol content of any wine chiefly depends on the length of time the grape skins are present during the fermentation process. Some red wines therefore contain more resveratrol than others. Better try them all. But before you do, be warned: doctors suggest that the greatest benefit to health comes from just one or two small glasses a day.

Communications

No, boss, I'm ill at home. Whatever it sounds like, I can't be at the big match, can I?

Imagine you're in a crowded pub, or out with someone you ought not to be, and your boss calls you on your mobile phone. The noise in the background would instantly betray your true whereabouts, and make it difficult for the caller to hear what you were saying over the din. But that could all be about to change if phone manufacturers adopt a phone design put forward in 2004 by American inventor Jaime Siegel of Woodcliff Hill, New Jersey. The gadget uses two micro-phones – one placed on the side of the phone closer to your face, and the other on the opposite side facing the noisy room or street. The mike closer to your face picks up what you say, plus the background noise, while the mike facing the room picks up mostly background noise. Now subtract one signal from the other ... and you eliminate a lot of the background noise.

Factoid:
'When people kiss, they both tilt their heads either to the left or to the right – it just depends on how they are positioned and how comfortable they are.'

FALSE
Not only do most people get into the habit of tilting to only one side when they kiss a partner but they may start off with a distinct preference for tilting that way in the first place. According to German researchers who secretly spied on kissing couples at railway sta-tions, airports, beaches and parks, people are twice as likely to tilt their heads *right* as opposed to left.

Non-human biology
Ecology

Trading in ivory is now severely restricted all over the world – isn't it?

Ivory trading is now almost entirely illegal, but there is one source of ivory that is perfectly within the law: the tusks of extinct mammoths! Mammoth ivory is of poorer quality than the elephant equivalent – it's very brittle and breaks easily, and also tends to smell – but business in it is booming. Between 1994 and 2001 70 tonnes of mammoth ivory was shipped into Hong Kong, just for distribution within China. Russia has meanwhile been exploiting mammoth ivory for over 200 years.

Diseases and disorders
Domestic events

What could be more attractive than magnets ... and swallowing them?

American radiologists in late 2004 warned parents of the dangers of swallowing more than one magnet at a time. Swallowing foreign objects is common among all children, but luckily, 80% of the swallowed objects pass harmlessly through the gastrointestinal system on their own, single magnets included. Consuming more than one magnet can spell disaster, however – because the magnets are attracted to each other across the walls of the intestines, with the result that loops of bowel become locked together. The ensuing life-threatening tangle can lead to tissue death and/or perforation of the intestinal wall.

Non-human biology
Ecology

Incautious human divers sometimes get the bends – but can marine creatures suffer too?

Scientists have discovered that sonar from ships and submarines might be causing sperm whales to get the bends. Whales were thought to be immune to this condition, more formally known as decompression sickness or caisson disease, but Michael Moore and Greg Early, from the Woods Hole Oceanographic Institutute in the United States, have found evidence of bone damage caused by the bends in the skeletons of a number of sperm whales, some from as long ago as the beginning of the twentieth century. The damage to the whales' bones is thought to be the result of surfacing too quickly which, just as in human scuba divers, causes tiny nitrogen bubbles to form in the blood, blocking small blood vessels and damaging the tissues they supply. The scientists think that whales, which often hunt for hours at a time at depths of getting on for 2 kilometres (over a mile) underwater, normally control their surfacing behaviour very carefully to prevent themselves from developing the bends. But if they are disturbed by underwater noises like sonar, explosions from sea-floor mapping, or even earthquakes, the whales may surface too quickly, and develop the condition. It's not just whales that are the victims, either. Recently, large numbers of dead giant squid have been washing up on beaches in South America with damaged ears, which is thought to be the result of exposure to underwater explosions detonated by companies surveying the sea floor for oil reserves.

Diseases and disorders
Food

Some drugs slow the effects of Alzheimer's, but is there any natural organic remedy?

Researchers in California have found that turmeric, the yellow spice added to curry and to some rice dishes, can block the formation of beta-amyloid, the abnormal protein which accumulates in the brains of patients with Alzheimer's disease. Turmeric, which is also known to have antioxidant and anti-inflammatory effects, has been linked previously to a reduced risk of Alzheimer's, and India, where it is a dietary staple, has the world's lowest rates of the disease. In the present study, Gregory Cole and his colleagues used mice genetically engineered to develop the mouse-equivalent of Alzheimer's. They found that the small molecular size of the turmeric compound allows it to penetrate brain tissues, mop up beta-amyloid, and break apart existing amyloid deposits, with greater efficiency than many other drugs being tested as Alzheimer treatments. For the moment and rather disappointingly, however, no clinical trials are currently being undertaken to establish what sorts of doses would be required in humans, or to quantify the effectiveness of turmeric's antioxidant and anti-inflammatory effects for the prevention of other conditions such as heart disease and cancer.

The mind
Human biology

Can I cut down on working out in the gym, and sit back and laugh instead?

Researchers at the University of Maryland School of Medicine have confirmed what the editors at *Readers Digest* have claimed for years – that laughter really is the best medicine. Michael Miller and his colleagues compared the response of the blood vessels of 20 healthy volunteers when they were shown a funny film, and when they were shown a mentally stressful film. The researchers used ultrasound to look at the function of the bloodvessel lining, called the endothelium, which plays a major role in regulating how relaxed, or open, blood vessels are. Damage to the endothelium is also linked to arterial disease. When the volunteers were shown the funny film, 19 out of the 20 showed beneficial relaxation of the blood vessels and their blood flow increased by 22%. But when they watched the mentally stressful film, 14 of the 20 study subjects showed a reduction in blood flow by an average of 35%, and changes in their bloodvessel reactivity persisted for up to 45 minutes afterwards. The changes the team saw with laughter were at least as great as those measured when people exercise. The research does not, however, reveal why the endothelium works less well to keep blood vessels open during mental stress, or why laughter is beneficial, but Miller suggests that it might be because stress in some way inhibits the production of the bloodvessel relaxant nitric oxide, which is secreted by the endothelium. The results of the study also agree with previous work published by the group in 2000, which showed that people with heart disease tended to respond with less humour to everyday situations than healthy individuals of the same age.

Culture

Communications

Culture – even in the form of Swedish poetry – is universal, isn't it?

Swedish poets decided in 2004 that citizens of other galaxies are in need of cultural enrichment, and beamed samples of their work into space in the direction of Vega, the brightest star in the constellation Lyra. Unfortunately, because Vega is about 26½ light years away, the poets will have to wait at least 53 years for any alien reviews to be forthcoming!

Food

I only use bottled water to dilute my drinks. Isn't it purer than tap water?

Don't be too sure. Bottled water is often considered to be purer than tap water – indeed, some hospitals give it to their patients in the belief that it is safer for them. But when Dr Rocus Klont and a team from the University of Nijmegen studied 68 commercially available mineral waters from nine European and seven non-European sources, they found that almost half – 40% of the samples – were contaminated with bacteria or fungi. Bacteria from 21 of the samples could actually be grown in the lab. Klont points out that whereas the contaminants in the water may pose only a limited threat to healthy people, in people at increased susceptibility to infection – such as patients with HIV or those on immunosuppressive drugs – the risks may be much greater.

Solar cell technology

Solar panels are rigid and don't work on cloudy days. Surely someone can improve on them?

Scientists from the University of Toronto have invented a flexible solar cell material that is five times more efficient than current methods of turning the sun's energy into electricity. Unlike existing solar cell technology, which uses visible light and is capable at best of turning 6% of the sun's energy into usable electrical energy, the new material engineered by Ted Sargent and his team harnesses infrared light and can capture 30% of the sun's power to produce electricity. And because it works on infrared, the new cell can produce electricity even on a cloudy day or in the dark since although visible light may be lacking, things that are warm – including people and animals – emit infrared radiation which the cell can use. An added bonus is that the new material is also highly flexible so it can be turned into a film to coat the surfaces of cloth, paper or other materials, potentially paving the way for wearable solar garments which Sargent terms 'portable electricity'. In this way you might soon be able to run your electronic gadgetry off your coat, or have a roll-up solar cell to help recharge your laptop, on the move. Sargent is intending to commercialise the invention which, he says, could be on the market within five to 10 years.

Plant biology
Ecology

Plants of the same species signal chemically to each other – but do different plants 'listen in'?

They certainly seem to. Methyl jasminate (which is actually a constituent of the famous Coco Chanel fragrance Chanel No. 5) is produced as a danger signal by a sagebrush shrub when it is attacked by herbivores. Sagebrush shrubs near by respond to this chemical alert by increasing the levels of their toxic defences, but other plants in the vicinity take note of the signal too. Cornell ecologist Andrew Kessler has found that tobacco plants grow much more rapidly when they are planted next to clipped sagebrush plants (which emit methyl jasminate) than when next to intact sagebrush. It seems that the chemical danger signal primes the tobacco to assume that it is itself about to be eaten, so it revs up its growth. This in turn leads to a boost in the levels of the precursors used by the tobacco plant to produce plant toxins, including nicotine. But to save resources, the plant only switches on the final step in the production line – to convert the precursors into the toxins – when the plant is physically attacked. Kessler believes that this chemical eavesdropping on the misfortunes of other plants is widespread in the green community.

Factoid:
'The atmosphere is coldest over the North Pole.'

FALSE
It's actually coldest 80 kilometres (50 miles) above the equator. The *warmest* atmospheric temperatures are found 300 kilometres (190 miles) above the poles, due to convection currents.

The mind
Human biology

'My brain's bigger than yours!'
'Oh yeah? And how're you going to prove it?'

'Size matters,' they say, but in the context of a developing child's brain, a larger quantity of grey matter evidently does not mean a higher intelligence. In the first study of its kind, researcher Peter Shaw, from the US Institute of Mental Health, brain-scanned more than 300 children, from the age of 6, several times as they grew up, and then compared each of the brain scans with the children's IQ tests. The results came as something of a surprise. The scans were designed to look at the sizes of different parts of the brain, and specifically the thickness of the cerebral cortex – the so-called 'grey matter' long associated with intelligence (particularly by one Hercule Poirot). Unexpectedly, the researchers found that the brightest children very often started with the least amount of grey matter, but then very quickly added much more until the age of eleven, before losing it again in adolescence. These changes were particularly marked in the prefrontal area – the region of the brain associated with reasoning, abstract thought and planning. As a result, it appears that the rate at which the brain can rearrange or re-organise its cortex, rather than the total amount of grey matter, seems to be the strongest determinant of how clever an individual will be. 'People with very agile minds tend to have a very agile cortex,' Shaw points out.

Non-human biology
Genetics

Can't we genetically modify mosquitoes to become vegetarians? Please?

Researchers David Denlinger and Rebecca Robich, from Ohio State University, have described how they tracked down three genes which control a mosquito's vampire-like taste for blood. During the summer months, when female mosquitoes lay eggs, they tend to feed on protein-rich blood. But as winter approaches they switch to consuming sugars collected from fruits in order to provide energy stores which enable them to survive during the winter. The trigger for this diet switch turns out to be the length of the day: as the number of hours of daylight declines, heralding the approach of winter, the insects start to bulk up for hibernation. By comparing which genes were switched on in either blood-sucking or sugar-quaffing mosquitoes, the researchers pinpointed two blood-digesting genes that are switched off, and a sugar and fat metabolising gene that is switched on, when the mosquitoes prepare for winter. By understanding better how these genes control the insect's behaviour it may be possible to use them to develop better disease control measures and prevent mosquitoes from making a meal of us in future.

Human biology
Food

Isn't there now some kind of chocolate that actually lowers body cholesterol?

The Mars confectionery company certainly hopes you have heard something about the CocoaVia™ range of snacks and bars it has been selling since 2005. They contain sterol plant extracts derived from soy and shown to be effective at reducing cholesterol levels. In a study before the launch of the first CocoaVia bar, 70 people with high cholesterol were randomly allocated to eat either two of the new cholesterol-reducing bars a day, or two placebo chocolate bars lacking any soy extracts. At the end of the six-week study period, compared with volunteers receiving the placebo chocolate snacks, study subjects eating the new bars had reduced their total cholesterol levels by nearly 5%, and their 'bad' cholesterol (LDL) levels by 6%. Critically, the levels of 'good' cholesterol, known as HDL, remained the same, reducing the patients' risks of heart disease. None of the subjects in either arm of the study showed any changes in weight or blood pressure. Although a 5% reduction in cholesterol doesn't sound like much, it could make the difference between a person's having to use cholesterol-lowering medication or not, particularly in combination with other cholesterol-lowering strategies like diet and weight loss. Another benefit of the CocoaVia bars is that they contain high levels of flavanols, a subclass of flavonoids (the antioxidants responsible for the health benefits associated with red wine, green tea, and green vegetables). According to Mars this is the first time that the combination of plant sterols and flavonoid antioxidants has been offered in a snack bar.

Vehicles

How do you guard against having your car keys stolen and then your car?

Car manufacturer DaimlerChrysler has come up with a security system to prevent stolen car keys from being used. Three separate radio receivers are plumbed into the car in three different places. When the 'unlock' button is pressed on the key fob, the signal takes a fractionally different amount of time to reach each receiver. Users can therefore 'personalise' the system by choosing a highly specific position in which to stand outside the car to unlock it. The receivers each log how long the signals take to reach them and thereafter the car will only unlock from that point. Would-be thieves who don't know the correct position will be unable to unlock the car, or deactivate the immobiliser.

Human biology
Gyroscopes

Isn't there a weight-training-like exercise that doesn't require weights?

California-based inventor William Dworzan has come up with a clever way to stay trim on holiday without the problem of carting dumbbells and weights around with you. His invention comprises a thin rod with handles at each end and a battery-powered gyroscope in the middle. An electric motor spins up the gyroscope, which holds the rod steady in a horizontal position. Because it takes a lot of effort to twist the gyroscopically-balanced rod from its horizontal position, it can be used as a heavy exercise device – all the workout without the weight.

Non-human biology
Dinosaurs

Is it possible to tell from fossils whether a dinosaur was male or female?

Researchers in the USA have devised a way to work out the sex of a dinosaur – something that has till now not been possible. The discovery hinges on many dinosaurs' closest living relatives: birds. As egg-layers, female birds need a large reserve of calcium to put into their egg shells, so calcium stores are laid down as an extra layer of bone on the insides of the birds' long bones. When the female needs a calcium boost, the minerals are quickly released from the bone into the bloodstream. This adaptation is absent from male birds because it is driven by the presence of female hormones, chiefly oestrogen. When scientists recently examined the small but well preserved skeleton of a *Tyrannosaurus rex*, they found structures similar to those seen in the long bones of female birds, suggesting that female dinosaurs also locked away their egg-laying calcium reserves in specialised bone structures. The finding will provide dinosaur experts with an objective way to determine the sex of the specimens they collect.

Factoid:
'If a child does not like eating vegetables, it may be because he or she is genetically programmed to dislike the taste.'

TRUE
According to recent research, 25% of the population are 'supertasters' and carry a gene that produces an increased number of taste buds on the tongue, causing them to dislike the bitter taste of brassicas (like cabbage, sprouts and broccoli) and young tomatoes.

Art history

X-rays and scanning

It's difficult enough spotting fake artworks – but how do you spot fake sculpture?

Researchers have found a way to use X-rays to weed out fake sculptures without harming them. Together with colleagues from France, Italian materials scientist Franco Rustichelli, from the Polytechnic University of the Marche in Ancona, has found that a technique called hard X-ray diffraction can be used to examine the crystal structure of metal and ceramic items, providing information about the casting process and composition of an artifact. By comparing this information with a database of known items it is possible to date objects, and also weed out fakes which, quite literally, break the mould. The technique works by shining a beam of high-energy X-rays at the object under scrutiny. The X-rays bounce off the crystals inside the object and then interfere with each other, producing a 'fingerprint' pattern related to the crystal architecture of the artifact. Objects which date from a similar period in history, or which were formed through a specific manufacturing process, have very similar crystal X-ray fingerprints whereas forgeries show a different pattern altogether. To prove the point the researchers tested two bronze castings, a Late Dynastic (1000–300 BC) ancient Egyptian statuette and an Etruscan figurine thought to date from 300 BC. The technique clearly distinguished between the two objects. A major benefit of this method is that previously, analyses of this type would have required the physical removal of a fragment of material from an artifact; using this method the items remain unharmed.

Animal biology

Histology

People say that clones are infertile – but is there any reason for them to be?

No. A successful clone is a true and perfect individual. Scientists in Italy have successfully cloned a gelded stallion, a world-class endurance champion named Pieraz, with the aim of using the un-gelded foal for breeding purposes!

Human biology

Have you no idea at all of what I mean when I snarl and frown and glare at you?

Professor David Skuse, from Imperial College London, has found a reason why teenagers make their parents lives a misery – because around the time of puberty they lose their ability to interpret facial expressions. By showing children between the ages of 7 and 17 pictures of faces bearing different expressions and asking the volunteers to comment on the likely mood of the person in the photo, Professor Skuse and his team have found a significant dip in the children's scores around the time of puberty. Females traditionally always out-perform males in this task, but the same result was seen amongst subjects of both sexes. The researchers now want to follow up a group of children for a number of years as they go through puberty in order to track any changes in their brains using a brain scanner, in order to work out why the effect occurs – and to shed light on how the brain decodes what others are thinking.

Culture

If you can now predict movie hits, how come there are so many dud movies still made?

Predicting whether a movie will be a box-office blockbuster or a miserable flop can make the difference between success and business ruin for producers and promoters and has traditionally been a difficult game to play. But now there is a new tool to help out. Ramesh Sharda, from Oklahoma State University, has developed an artificial neural network that can sort out what is hot from what is not, in the world of film. The system, which was set up using data from 834 films shown between 1998 and 2002, considers seven key movie parameters in order to assign a box-office smash score. These are: the 'star value' of the film (in other words, which actors play the lead roles), the age certificate, the competition (which may be a matter of good or bad luck, depending on what else is released simultaneously), the genre of the flick (if it is about French history, for example, it may go down well at Cannes but nowhere else), the special effects, how many screens it will be shown on, and whether it is a sequel. The system uses this data to assign the film to one of nine categories ranging from 'flop', grossing less than a million dollars, to 'blockbuster', taking over 200 million dollars. According to Sharma, his system gets the revenue category absolutely right 37% of the time, and is correct to within one category either side at least 75% of the time. He is now working on expanding the system to look at DVD sales too.

Physics
Geology

Even when compass north is actually south, we can still use our old compass, can't we?

The strength of the Earth's magnetic field has decreased by 10% over the last 150 years, raising the possibility that it might be about to collapse and reverse so that the south pole actually becomes the magnetic north pole! At the current rate of decline our magnetic field could vanish within 1,500 to 2,000 years before re-establishing itself with the poles reversed. This is not a new phenomenon – the Earth has been flipping its magnetic field about every 200,000 years in the past, but the last flip was over 800,000 years ago, so we are well overdue for it to happen again. But scientists are sceptical that it will come to that at the moment ... although over the southern Atlantic Ocean, a continued weakening of the magnetic field has diminished the shielding effect it has locally in protecting the Earth from the natural radiation that bombards our planet from space. As a result, satellites in low Earth orbit are left vulnerable to that radiation as they pass over the region known as the South Atlantic Anomaly. Among the satellites that have fallen prey to the harmful effects was a Danish satellite designed, ironically, to measure the Earth's magnetic field. The weakening of our magnetic field may also contribute to the loss of the Earth's protective ozone layer which shields us from the cancer-causing effects of ultraviolet rays.

Medicine

Diseases and disorders

To avoid heart failure, can't the heart be physically prevented from enlarging?

When patients develop heart failure, one of the first signs is that the heart enlarges and begins to pump less efficiently. Reducing the size of the heart, or preventing it from becoming enlarged in the first place, can lead to improvements in heart function. Since 2004, doctors from St Louis University School of Medicine have been testing the cardiac equivalent of a string bag made from polyester mesh, which can be surgically implanted all around the heart to prevent it from enlarging. A large trial involving 300 patients found that the 148 who received the 'heart jacket' improved significantly.

Sleep

Human biology

Why does the alarm clock always ring when you feel like sleeping on for ever?

Tired of waking up feeling like you haven't even been to bed? Then a new alarm clock that reads your brain waves to pinpoint the best time to wake you up – so that (in theory, at least) you rise feeling fresh and raring to go – could be for you. Sleepsmart, as it is known, was the brainchild of students at Brown University in Rhode Island. It works on the principle that if people are woken up when they are in the lightest phase of sleep, they feel much more alert than if they are woken from deep sleep.

Ecology
Domestic events

Who could imagine that garlic might turn out to be an environmentally-friendly pesticide?

Scientists at Newcastle University have found that garlic (*Allium sativum*) could be used to rid your garden of slugs and snails without risking the health of your dogs, cats or other animals that might accidentally eat the traditional slug pellets. The researchers took a leaf out of the books of medieval monks who, for hundreds of years, used to grow garlic close to their crops because they knew it would ward off pests. Ingo Schuder and Gordon Port, who carried out the research, found that spraying Chinese cabbage (*Brassica rapa pekinensis*, also called pe-tsai) leaves with garlic extracts prevented them from being eaten, and killed many of the slugs and snails that tried. Plants could also be protected by spraying the extract onto soil which stopped pests reaching the crops. The obvious benefit of using a natural plant extract like this is that it is much safer than using artificial chemicals. On the other hand it has the possible disadvantage of altering the flavour of foods. Although we don't yet know why garlic kills slugs and snails, it probably affects the animals' nervous system. The researchers are now testing whether garlic could be used commercially by farmers to protect their crops, and trying to prove that garlic will not damage the environment.

Non-human biology
Human biology

Don't long periods of inactivity dangerously weaken bones in both humans and animals?

In general, yes. But black bears seem to be unique amongst
hibernating animals because they have the unique ability to
stop their bones from thinning during their long winter sleep
– suggesting that they may hold the key to preventing
bone-thinning diseases like osteoporosis in humans. Usually,
any period of prolonged inactivity without weight-bearing
exercise, including being immobile, elderly or even going
into space, can lead to significant bone loss. But by studying
the metabolism of hibernating bears, Seth Donahue and his
colleagues from Michigan Technological University have
found that unlike people and other animals, bears keep laying
down new bone even when they are inactive. The researchers
think that this is because, unlike most hibernating animals,
bears do not urinate or defecate. They have no way to get rid
of waste calcium from the body – so instead, they put it into
their bones. To find out how they do this the researchers are
now looking for differences between humans and bears
amongst some of the key hormones that regulate bone density
and calcium metabolism. This may lead to new therapies for
the prevention or reversal of human bone loss. Osteoporosis
is a serious problem: around 50% of women and 25% of men
over the age of 50 suffer a fracture because of it.

Factoid:
'A mosquito could drain the blood from a human adult
with ten million bites.'

FALSE
Rather scarily, it would take about a tenth of that
number – just over a million bites – to drain your
blood. But you'd probably notice before then.

Electricity
Domestic events

Is the UK Government going to extend power to the people?

A UK-based not-for-profit company, Dynamic Demand, has come up with a way to make appliances less energy-hungry at times when the national power grid is struggling to keep up with demand. Their strategy involves giving appliances the ability to monitor how much load the grid is experiencing, and then to cut power usage when things look sticky. The system is elegantly simple: it merely involves monitoring the frequency of the electricity arriving in homes and offices, which is kept close to 50 Hz (cycles per second). When energy demand becomes high, however, the turbines in powerstations slow down very slightly, dropping the frequency – to, say, 49.5 Hz. Dynamic Demand exploits this drop to enable power-hungry gadgets like air-conditioners, boilers or other non-essential items to switch themselves off, or drop their power rating temporarily. At the moment national grids across the world run a series of standby generators which can power up and down to help smooth out spikes in demand, but keeping them running uses large amounts of energy, is inefficient, and produces large amounts of carbon dioxide as a result. The Dynamic Demand approach could help to change all that. As a result, a bill has now been presented to Parliament calling for the UK Goverment to take the matter seriously.

Human biology

The mind

A brain centre for sarcasm? Oh sure – I'm really going to believe that, aren't I?

Researchers from Israel's University of Haifa have described how they homed in on the part of the brain responsible for comprehending sarcasm. The team compared the ability of two groups of patients with brain injuries to understand sarcastic comments. One group had damage to the front-most part of the brain, known as the prefrontal cortex, whereas the second group had damage to structures further back in the brain. The patients with damage to the prefrontal cortex, and particularly the region known as the right ventromedial prefrontal cortex (just above the right eye), had the most difficulty understanding sarcastic remarks. It is a finding that fits with what we already know about this part of the brain which seems to be heavily involved in complex social interactions, personality and pragmatic language processing.

Non-human biology

Surely 'wagging' is a side-to-side movement and can only be horizontal?

People curious about what mood their dog is in can purchase a 'wagometer' which analyses the wag of the tail to determine whether the dog is happy or not. According to the inventor of the device, Dr Roger Mugford, a happy dog tends to have a wide and horizontal wag.

Physics
Human biology

Amazing, isn't it, that simply breathing can provide damning evidence against you?

Anti-terror squads could soon have a new weapon at their disposal to help track down bombers: a breathalyser that can pick up signs of handling explosives. Dubbed Heartsbreath, the new device – which has been developed by Michael Phillips and his colleagues from Menssana Research in New Jersey – is said to be a billion times more sensitive than the ordinary breathalyser used by traffic cops, and can detect minute traces of explosive compounds exhaled on the breath of individuals who have recently handled ordnance, including dynamite, TNT and C-4. The machine was originally developed to assist in medical diagnosis, looking for volatile compounds produced by lung cancers and in cases of incipient heart-transplant rejection. But because explosive chemicals can be inhaled or absorbed through the skin, the developers wondered whether the machine could also pick up these chemical signatures too. The researchers admit there is some way to go before this approach becomes a front-line tool in the war against terrorism, but they are optimistic that it could provide a rapid and sensitive way to flush out would-be bombers, including possibly picking up signs of radiation exposure.

Evolution

Did Darwin suddenly dream up his theory, or did it just ... evolve?

Ever since Darwin penned his famous book *On the Origin of Species*, scientists have been searching for evidence that one of Darwin's suggestions – that a new species might originate amongst an existing one – is true. While it is well accepted that new species come along when geography intervenes and separates one group of organisms from another so that over time the two populations become genetically distinct from one another, examples of Darwin's other suggestion have not been forthcoming ... until now. Now, two papers – one looking at palm trees on an island off Australia, and the other looking at fish living in a crater lake in Nicaragua – have proved that Darwin was absolutely right (again). Researcher Vincent Savolainen, from Kew Gardens in London, found that two species of palm tree on Lord Howe Island, off the southeast coast of the Australian mainland, are genetically very close relatives and must have split away from each other *after* they arrived at the island group. The two tree species prefer slightly different soil types and now flower at different times of the year. Meanwhile in the Nicaraguan crater lake, Konstanz University's Axel Meyer has found a unique species of cichlid fish alongside a close relative. That the unique species was not found in any other lake they tested, and prefers to live in open water compared with its shore-loving relative, proves that the fish must have evolved recently (within the last 10,000 years or less) side by side with its relatives. Aside from permitting Darwin a smug grin in his grave, and settling a 150-year-old argument, these findings have implications for our understanding of how new species emerge, including humans.

Non-human biology
Ecology

So it's not just humans who have 'their own special tree', then, is it?

Ants choose their plants wisely, it seems. According to one study, Megan Frederickson and her colleagues at Stanford University in California have found that an Amazonian species of tree-nesting ants, scientifically described as *Myrmelachista schumanni*, which set up home in the hollow stems of a tree called *Duroia hirsuta*, actively poison all the other plants near by, leaving just their preferred species of tree alive. Initially, it was thought that the tree itself might be preventing the growth of other species near by, but when the researchers planted saplings of a different species in their midst they found that the ants promptly turned on the impostors and killed them by injecting formic acid from their stings into the leaves. The findings explain a longstanding conundrum of why large areas of Amazonian rainforest, traditionally believed to be the work of an evil spirit and known colloquially as Devil's gardens, are made up almost entirely from this single tree species.

Factoid:
'If all the passengers on an aircraft suddenly jumped up off the floor, the plane would very briefly weigh less.'

FALSE
The weight of the plane would very briefly *increase* because of the force exerted on the floor of the aircraft by the passengers in the act of jumping.

Genetics

Diseases and disorders

Will advances in gene therapy make a difference to the treatment of haemophiliacs?

US researchers have successfully used gene therapy to treat a group of human sufferers of the bleeding disorder haemophilia B. The University of Pennsylvania's Catherine Manno and her colleagues have used a genetically modified virus to add a working version of a gene for the blood clotting protein called Factor IX, which is missing from the blood of patients with this form of haemophilia. The team used a virus known as an adeno-associated virus in which they had replaced the normal viral genetic material with the Factor IX gene. The virus was injected into the hepatic artery – which supplies blood to the liver – in seven patients. The viral particles were then carried to the liver where they entered a number of liver cells and inserted their clotting gene cargo into the patients' DNA. Encouragingly, the patients that received the highest viral doses began to produce detectable levels of Factor IX in their blood, although the effect was only temporary and persisted for only two months. The researchers believe that this was the consequence of the immune system slowly removing the liver cells that were infected by the virus, suggesting that longer treatment might be possible if drugs are given to control the immune system. Significantly, this study proves that a modified virus can be used to safely deliver therapeutic genes to the liver, potentially sparing haemophiliacs the inconvenience of daily injections with costly blood-clotting replacements.

Medicine
Domestic events
Food

Tea is often described as 'reviving' – but does it really have medicinal properties?

Daniel Fung from Kansas State University has found that extracts from a variety of teas – including green tea, oolong tea and jasmine tea – can kill some of the germs responsible for causing food poisoning, among them certain strains of *Salmonella* and *Listeria*. But tea extracts clearly aren't the answer to everything because some types of *Salmonella*, and *E. coli* were not affected by tea treatment. Nor did the researchers test their extracts against one of the most common types of food poisoning bug: *Campylobacter*.

Communications

You mean, I can achieve intergalactic fame ... so long as I stay polite?

American company Mindcomet, seriously concerned that extraterrestrials might get a bad impression of humankind from the atrociously violent TV and radio transmissions that we inadvertently beam into space, has launched a free service – bloginspace.com – to beam people's personal Internet diaries (blogs) into space. The idea is to present our species in a different light to any aliens out there who might be listening. Naturally, they are urging contributors to refrain from using any language or content that might offend off-world eavesdroppers!

Astronomy

Isn't it hard to remember that the stars in the sky are at different distances *and times* away?

One of the universe's first stars, which was shining over 12.8 billion years ago, just 800 million years after the Big Bang, has been spotted by researchers from the USA, Europe and Japan. With the help of the SWIFT satellite, a joint UK, Italian and American initiative launched in 2004 to track gamma-ray bursts (GRBs) which occur when stars explode, researchers including the University of North Carolina's Dan Reichart, and the Tokyo Institute of Technology's Nobuyaki Kawai, spotted a GRB mapping to a massive stellar convulsion that took place nearly 13 billion years ago. By analysing the light emitted from the explosion, the researchers were able to determine that the star was a giant of at least 30 times the mass of our own sun, and had created a rich supply of oxygen, silicon and metals that had been released to provide the raw materials for complex chemistry in future worlds and stars. The discovery makes this early star one of the most distant ever sighted, and has shed further light on our understanding of the early universe.

Factoid:

'Inexorable continental drift means that Britain and North America are separating from each other by about 25 millimetres (I inch) a year.'

FALSE

They are moving apart, but only by about 10 millimetres (two-fifths of an inch) a year – or at about the same rate that your fingernails grow over the same period!

Palaeontology
Geology

If climate change caused apes to stand upright as bipeds, what caused the climate change?

A team of German scientists examining material from the sea bed beneath the Pacific Ocean think that they may have uncovered an important clue to the processes that kick-started the evolution of humankind. Drilling 4,800 metres (15,750 feet) below the surface, Günther Korschinek and his colleagues from the Munich Technical University (Technische Universität München) have found deposits dating back about 3 million years of a rare form of iron called iron-60, which is normally only found in exploding stars and thus, in the decayed form of nickel-60, in meteorites that land on Earth. The discovery of these rare iron deposits indicates that a massive explosion occurred close to the Earth around the same time that our earliest ancestors evolved. The team believe that such an explosion would have bombarded the Earth for up to 300,000 years in cosmic rays sufficiently strong to alter the climate. At precisely this time in Africa the climate did change quite abruptly – it became drier, the forests retreated, and the savannah opened up. As they lost their forest homes, our ancestors were pushed out of the trees, on to the ground ... and then up on to two legs ...

Domestic events
Medicine
Human biology

What could be more beneficially relaxing than a steaming cup of coffee and a cigarette?

Greek researchers have announced that the habit of starting the day with a coffee and a cigarette may be extra hard on your arteries. Dr Charalambos Vlachopoulos from the Athens Medical School in Greece – a man who has also investigated the health-giving properties of chocolate – studied the arterial stiffness of 24 young healthy adults when they smoked a cigarette, drank a cup of coffee, or did both. The study showed that the combination of caffeine and smoking made the body's main blood vessel – the aorta, leading directly from the heart towards most of the rest of the body – temporarily stiffer than either drug alone, or added together. In other words, the effects of the two drugs together multiply, rather than add up, and may contribute to increased harm to the arteries in the long term. Indeed, a second, larger, study involving 160 adults found that those who were regular cigarette and coffee consumers showed the greatest blood vessel stiffness. Stiffer blood vessels elevate blood pressure, make the heart work harder to push blood around the body, and therefore increase the risk of developing heart disease and stroke.

Colour
The senses
Sociology

OK, Manchester fans, why does the team in red seem to win more than the team in blue?

Scientists from the UK's University of Durham have announced that the soccer players of world-famous Manchester United would do better always to play in red (despite the Football Association's current insistence on different home and away strips) because they are then statistically much more likely to win. The researchers analysed the outcomes of four combat sports from the Athens 2004 Olympics – boxing, tae kwon-do, Graeco-Roman wrestling and freestyle wrestling – and found that participants competing in red were significantly and consistently more likely to win against opponents clad in blue. Analysis of a series of soccer games from Euro 2004 also turned up the same results. The researchers put the findings down to redness being a testosterone-fuelled masculine signal used throughout nature as a sign of dominance, anger, danger and aggression. Fear, on the other hand, is associated more with a bluish pallor. Competitors wearing red may therefore be influencing a primitive part of their opponents' brain which is programmed to be awed by redness. Tough, Manchester City and Carlton fans.

Genetics

Diseases and disorders

Will advances in gene therapy ever come close to curing blindness?

Scientists from Manchester University and Imperial College in England have discovered that human nerve cells can be made light-sensitive by activating a gene for a light-sensitive substance called melanopsin. This finding, although not specifically indicating a potential cure for blindness, could nonetheless lead to therapies for certain forms of sight loss including retinitis pigmentosa, a hereditary condition that causes the destruction of the rods and cones, the light-sensitive elements of the retina.

Human biology

How is it possible that girls are attracted to boys who show off? Or aren't they?

All lads show off in front of women, whether it's behind the wheel of a car, on a skateboard, or with a surfboard. But recent research from the USA suggests that although men are convinced that women will be impressed by risk-taking behaviour, women actually prefer their potential consorts to be more cautious – or should that be less stupid? So ditch the fast car for something sensible, and see if your luck changes!

Dentistry

Human biology

It's all very well smiling *after* going to the dentist, but who can smile on the way there?

Comforting news! Japanese dentistry researchers have developed a new material for fillings that greatly reduces any need for the dentist's drill! The cement-like amalgam-equivalent latches on to damaged tooth surfaces and integrates itself seamlessly into the tooth structure, producing an invisible mend. Tooth decay (caries) occurs when acid produced by mouth bacteria eats into the enamel surfaces of teeth, producing small pits. Dentists currently have to enlarge the hole, drilling away healthy tooth material, in order to provide a secure socket for the filling material because it does not adhere perfectly to the enamel surface. But the new material is a paste made of hydroxyapatite – a form of calcium phosphate – exactly the same substance that makes up the enamel itself. When the paste is added to a damaged tooth, it sets within minutes, sealing off the affected area and bonding immaculately to the tooth surface. Even viewed under a microscope the repair is invisible. The researchers suggest that because the paste is quite acidic it initially dissolves some of the native tooth enamel before forming new crystals which lock themselves into the tooth surface in a smooth, homogeneous layer. The method not only repairs decayed teeth but can also strengthen them, preventing the problem from recurring.

Computer technology
Robots

Multiplication: that's the name of the game – but what's the point for a computer?

US researchers report that they have produced a robot that can make functional copies of itself. The robot consists of a series of identical cubes that can rotate about their diagonals and can selectively stick to each other using electromagnets. In the same way that most human cells carry a complete copy of human genetic material, each cube comes complete with a computer program telling it how to co-operate with other cubes to form a robot and replicate. Given a ready supply of food (more of the same cubes), the robot can build a copy of itself. Although this robot has no genuine individual application, it is an important proof of the concept, which researchers say they hope will pave the way for the production of robots capable of self-assembly and repair for use in space or other extreme environments.

Factoid:
'Mice are super-intelligent – on forays in unfamiliar territory they leave trails in order to find their way back safely and quickly.'

TRUE
Scientists at Oxford University have found that mice often leave piles of seeds, twigs or shells to help them find their way home in confusing places like large fields of crops. Leaving visual signals like this is thought to be safer than scent-marking which a predator could pick up.

Human biology
Histology

Do we know how individual body cells 'switch on' and do what they do?

Scanners could be about to get a whole lot more detailed now that researchers have worked out how to spot when individual genes are turning on and off inside single cells. This discovery will enable scientists to non-invasively track how cells communicate with each other, how memories are laid down, and how cells 'decide' what to become in a developing embryo.

Non-human biology
Australia

Dolphins are clever. How come they haven't got round to using tools, then?

Some have. According to one report, dolphins living in Shark Bay, Western Australia, wear conically-shaped whole sponges, which they tear off the bottom, to protect their noses while they forage on the sea bed. Dolphins involved in the practice – dubbed 'spongers' by the researchers – seem to be overwhelmingly female, and to pass the idea on to their daughters who presumably learn the trick by watching their mothers. And the males? According to the same researchers, the males are too busy foraging for females to waste time poking around on the sea bed. Clearly, dolphins are a lot more like humans than we give them credit for!

Food

Human biology

'Eat fat, become fat' – but actually, there are even worse consequences, aren't there?

Scientists have shown that eating fatty food not only clogs up your blood vessels but is also bad for your brain. Rats and mice fed the rodent equivalent of nothing but junk food for two months were less mentally agile and had significantly worse memories compared with normally-nourished animals. The rats and mice were tested on their abilities to find their way around mazes, and to locate platforms hidden just below the surface of a pool of water. Animals on high-fat diets took much longer to learn the tasks, and made many more mistakes, than their healthier counterparts. The researchers blame the poor performance on high levels of triglycerides in the bloodstream of the fat-rats, because when a group of animals were given a triglyceride-lowering drug, their memories improved. Memory problems similar to that experienced by the rats has also been documented in diabetics with high triglyceride levels, although it remains to be seen whether the same is true in healthy human subjects. The researchers do point out, in the meantime, that raised triglyceride levels in humans are all too commonly caused by the presence of trans-fatty acids which are popular with food manufacturers because they prolong a product's shelf-life.

Medicine
Diseases and disorders

Will it ever be possible to use a scanner to detect a virus?

To some extent it can be done already. Scientists from Harvard University in the USA have devised a detector which can rapidly identify some viruses in patient samples. Charles Lieber and his team have found a way to link tiny silicon wires, so small as to be described as nanowires, to antibodies which can lock on to specific viruses. When the antibodies pick up a virus, or even part of a virus, the electrical conductance of the wires changes in a characteristic way for that particular virus. In other words, different viruses produce their own specific electrical fingerprint which enables the machine to identify, immediately, which viruses are present in a sample collected from a patient. So far the technique has worked successfully on flu viruses, adenoviruses and a member of the mumps (infectious parotitis) virus family. The major benefit is the speed with which the machine can help a doctor reach a diagnosis. Present methods involve sending patient samples to a laboratory where they are painstakingly cultured, subjected to DNA analysis, or identified under the microscope, often with the aid of colour-coded antibodies. The whole process is very labour-intensive and time-consuming. But the new nanowire technique can in addition detect several different infections simultaneously, again saving time, and patients also receive appropriate treatment for their infections more rapidly – including being isolated from other patients to whom they might pose an infection risk.

Plant biology
Physics

Did you really think those fluorescent night-jackets were just to make people visible?

A group of Spanish researchers has found that certain night-blooming flowers might deploy an additional lure for pollinators including bees and bats – the ability to glow in the dark. Fernando Gandia-Herrero and his colleagues extracted the pigments from *Mirabilis jalapa* flowers and found that one of them – yellow betaxanthin – can soak up blue light to make itself glow green. The petals of the plant also create alluring patterns by adding (apparently only in certain places) a second substance, called betanin, which can nullify the fluorescence to make those parts of the leaf look dark. Budgerigars and shrimps are known to set high store by the fluorescence of their partners, but this is the first time that a plant has been found to resort to the floral equivalent of a fluorescent jacket to get noticed in the mating game!

Factoid:
'A person with an IQ of 100 is rather more intelligent than average.'

FALSE
An IQ of 100 is intended precisely to represent the average intelligence. People with an IQ below 100 are accordingly said to have below-average intelligence, and those with an IQ above 100 are said to be of above-average intelligence.

Histology
Human biology

Is there any way of avoiding the controversial aspects of stem cell research?

The therapeutic potential of stem cells for humans is huge, but many people object on the grounds that embryos are often required to produce them. But now Karl Swann and his team from the University of Cardiff have found a way to fool unfertilised eggs into thinking that they have been fertilised by a sperm, and beginning the process of cell division, and hence stem cell production, a process known as parthenogenesis. The key to the trick involves injecting the egg with an enzyme from sperm called phospholipase-C zeta (PLC-zeta). Normally, the sperm carries this enzyme into the egg, signalling fertilisation. But because no sperm have been used, the egg contains only DNA from the mother and hence cannot turn into a baby, which should allay the fears of people concerned about the ethics of using embryos as a source of human spare parts. Another potential spin-off of the project is the possibility that it might help people trying to become pregnant by in-vitro fertilisation (IVF). Very often, embryos created by fertilising eggs with sperm in a test-tube fail to begin to divide, possibly because the sperm have defective phospholipase-C zeta. Adding the enzyme artificially might help to kick-start division, boosting the chances of IVF success.

The senses
Robots

Guide dogs are wonderful, but they are ... dogs. Couldn't a robot 'dog' do better?

Engineers at the University of Utah have come up with an electronic guide dog which takes cues from hidden beacons concealed in the environment to help visually-impaired people find their way around foreign environments, such as airports, or locate the right shelves in shops; in other words, in situations in which a normal guide dog would be less helpful. The user need only select a destination from a Braille directory on the robot, and he or she is at once escorted directly there. Upon arrival the 'dog' can then provide more specialised information – such as where to find the toothpaste.

Microwave technology
Human biology

Lasers are not normally used for crowd control – but what about microwaves?

US defence researchers are road-testing a vehicle-mounted microwave weapon designed to 'cook' crowds into submission. The advanced denial system or ADS fires a narrow microwave beam at a frequency of 95 GHz over a range of 700 metres/yards. When the beam hits flesh, it rapidly heats the skin, triggering intense pain and encouraging the target to move away. According to reports, a two-second burst from the device can heat the skin surface to 50°C(122°F), producing excruciating pain but *without damaging or burning tissue.*

Human biology
Far East

Asian flu is highly infectious – but what about Asian laughter?

Concerned about surging levels of depression among the 7 million residents of Hong Kong, in mid-July 2005 the Joyful Mental Health Foundation organised a laughing contest in the city to raise people's spirits. Contestants were judged on how long they could laugh, and the effect of their laughter on others. Teams of up six people were allowed. According to one of the organisers, the judges were instructed to look for 'the quality of the laughter, whether it is infectious, and genuine'.

Electricity

Power cuts are a pain. What's the biggest power-cut backup system now?

The *Guinness Book of Records* has acknowledged a new contender for the largest battery ever built. Weighing 1,300 tonnes, covering an area larger than a soccer field, and made up of 13,760 nickel-cadmium cells linked together, ABB-Saft's installation in Alaska is a record-breaker. It has been installed in Fairbanks, Alaska, as a backup system for the local power grid, notorious for power cuts which, with temperatures around −50 Celsius, are no laughing matter! The new battery, christened BESS (for Battery Energy Storage System) can provide 27 Megawatts of power for 15 minutes and handle heavier demands of up to 46 Megawatts for shorter periods – generally enough to keep 10,000 homes running until normal service is resumed!

Astronomy

Is the Hubble telescope permanently trained on the furthest reaches of the universe?

Not at all. Thanks to the sharp eyes of the Hubble Space Telescope, researchers have spotted two new moons in orbit around the solar system's own outermost planet, Pluto. Excitingly christened S/2005 P1 and S/2005 P2, the new satellites – which orbit at a distance of 30,000 to 40,000 miles (48,000–64,000 kilometres) from the planet – join Charon, Pluto's first known moon, which is so relatively large as to be virtually a 'companion planet'. The discovery was announced by researchers Alan Stern and Hal Weaver who focused Hubble on the area around Pluto and watched as two tiny pinpricks of light came into view. The moons were not spotted before because they are so much smaller than Charon, whose light easily hides their presence. Because all three moons circle Pluto in the same plane, the researchers believe that they all formed together, rather than being the result of Pluto's capturing pieces of passing debris. Exactly how they formed is still something of a mystery, although researchers believe that planet and moons are probably the end result of a cosmic collision between two Pluto-sized objects. To further explore these theories, Weaver and Stern plan to focus Hubble back on Pluto throughout 2006 to look for any other moons and also to determine the size, shape and composition of the new discoveries, which should also shed welcome light on how the Plutonian system may have formed.

Sociology

Food

Is it true that people who go to church tend to spend more days on Earth than others?

Researchers have known for some time that statistically, people who go to church tend to live longer, but now a new study on churchgoers' eating habits provides one possible explanation as to why – because regular church attenders eat more healthily. Deirdre Griffith and her colleagues at the St Louis University School of Public Health compared the diets of frequent church attenders with those of non-churchgoers. They found that people who frequently go to church eat on average 26% more 'powerhouse' fruits and vegetables – those containing the most nutrients – than their less pious counterparts. They say your body is a temple, so it's ironic that going to church apparently helps you treat it that way! But it's a little early to conclude that religiously going to church improves your diet – the findings could be biased by any number of different factors. After all, the very exercise and activity of going to church must create a heartier appetite for wholesome food than lazing at home all day snacking and raiding the fridge for packaged meals. Social class in some areas may also be influential, those in higher social classes, who are known to eat better and live longer, being more likely to go to church.

Factoid:
'The neon of neon tube lighting is a kind of gas.'

TRUE
Neon is one of the so-called noble gases and is used in electric lights and signs because when it is excited by electricity it produces a bright and continuous glow.

Diseases and disorders
Drugs and drug abuse

A lot of research is being carried out into Alzheimer's. Any advances in drug treatments?

A team of researchers at the University of California, Irvine, led by Professor Frank LaFerla, has described a drug capable of halting the progression of Alzheimer's disease in mice which have been genetically programmed to develop the condition. A characteristic feature of Alzheimer's is the loss of a class of nerve cells which use the chemical acetylcholine – a substance instrumental in the transmission of nerve impulses. The new agent, known as AF267B, is able to mimic this missing neuro-transmitter, thereby reducing the symptoms of the disease, but it seems also to be able to halt the development of two other key pathological characteristics of Alzheimer's: the accumulation of toxic tangles inside nerve cells, called PHF tau, and protein aggregates called amyloid plaques. A Californian bio-tech company, Torrey-Pines Therapeutics, has been conducting a clinical trial to confirm the safety of the agent for use in humans. In early tests the drug appears to have been well tolerated amongst a group of healthy males, although it remains to be seen whether it will work as well in humans with dementia as it has done in the Alzheimer's mice.

Solar technology
Electricity

Electricity generation – can it really all be done with mirrors?

Engineers at Stirling Energy Systems reflecting on the best way to boost energy production in California – where solar energy already competes with more traditional contributors to the state power grid – have come up with a plan to blanket thousands of hectares of desert with mirrors. The 11-metre (36-foot) wide giants will focus the sun's rays onto a central engine comprising a series of cylinders filled with hydrogen. The light relected from the array of mirrors will heat the hydrogen to over 700° Celsius (1,300°F), causing it to expand and force down a piston in each cylinder. The falling piston drives a generator, which produces electricity, and at the same time the hot gas escapes and cool gas flows in to replace it. The whole process converts solar energy to electrical energy with an efficiency of about 30% – roughly twice as much as that achievable with solar cells (photovoltaic cells). At the end of 2005 two plants were under construction: one near Los Angeles, which will produce about 500 Mw, and a smaller version outside San Diego, which will pump out about 300 Mw.

The senses
Human biology

Why do you recoil when I lean over to talk confidentially to you?

Israeli scientists have found a way to banish bad breath for good – with a laser. Most cases of bad breath, or halitosis, result from the presence of stinky gases like hydrogen sulphide that are pumped out by bacteria living in crevices between the teeth and at the gum margins. A trip to the dentist, together with careful brushing and flossing, usually solves the problem. But there are some rarer cases (about 6%) which are more difficult to treat, and Yehuda Finkelstein, from the Sapir Medical Centre in Kfar, Israel, has pinpointed the tonsils as the cause, and found that a quick blast with a laser can remedy the situation. In these situations, bacteria multiply deep within grooves in the tonsils known as crypts. Laser therapy works by abrading the surface of the tonsils, provoking the formation of scar tissue, sealing off the crypts so bacteria can no longer multiply there. In an initial trial of 53 patients, over half were cured following their first treatment and the rest after two or three sessions. However, before you opt for the laser, dentists advise that you try more conventional therapies first – such as scraping your tongue, drinking plenty of water, tooth flossing, and mouthwashes.

Factoid:
'In smoking cigarettes, what may cause cancer is the nicotine.'

FALSE
Nicotine is what makes cigarettes addictive. What might cause cancer is the tars the cigarettes contain, which are produced by burning the tobacco.

Astronomy

Geology

No one seems to be bringing back moondust any more. What's happened to space geology?

The Japan Aerospace Exploration Agency (JAXA) has reported that Hayabusa – its mission to land on and retrieve a sample from 25143 Itokawa, a 540-metre (1,770-foot) long potato-shaped asteroid drifting about 188 million miles (300 million kilometres) from Earth – has been at least partly successful. The craft was launched in May 2003 and arrived in the vicinity of the asteroid in September 2005. But problems with the landing gear meant that the success of the mission hung in the balance. However, in November, mission control announced that the probe had fired two metal projectiles into the asteroid's surface to liberate surface particles that were (it is hoped) then collected and stored for the return to Earth. Leaving Itokawa, the probe encountered further technical problems including engine trouble which were thought to jeopardise the mission. But scientists now believe that those problems have been resolved, and Hayabusa – which means 'peregrine falcon' – is currently scheduled to return to Earth in June 2010 (when it is expected to parachute-land somewhere near Woomera, Australia). With luck, it will be bringing with it the first pristine samples ever collected from an asteroid, which should help to shed some fresh light on the creation of our solar system.

Military technology
Aircraft

Robot spy-planes are common in the movies, but do they actually exist?

Developers in Israel have come up with the Steadi-copter, an unmanned helicopter. The unpiloted craft, described as a UAV or unmanned aerial vehicle, uses clever computer software and global positioning satel-lite technology to fly without any human intervention. This means that anyone, trained pilot or not, can control it from a remote location. If the aircraft loses contact with its operator it can also continue and complete its mission automatically. At the moment the prototype consists of a 1.7-metre-long (5-foot) mini-copter – but, says the company, the system will work with any helicopter from hobby-sized to military.

Diseases and disorders
Human biology

They say depressed people take longer to recover from illness. Is that true?

In a study of over 80 male and female students who were vaccinated against the flu, those who scored most highly on a 'loneliness survey' and had the most restricted social networks mounted the weakest anti-body responses, making them more susceptible to the flu than their less lonely counterparts. These findings could also help to explain why first-year students tend to be ill more often than older students – because they feel socially 'unanchored', making them more suscep-tible to infection.

Ecology
Non-human biology

A prince in the guise of a frog, yes, but what's the point of a frog looking like another frog?

Imitation may be the sincerest form of flattery, but not when it comes to toxicity, it seems. University of Texas researcher Catherine Darst has found that where the ranges of two species of poison arrow frogs overlap in the Ecuadorian Amazon rain forest, other non-toxic frogs are imitating their bright colour schemes to deceive predators partial to a frog-sized meal into leaving them alone. Stealing the danger signals of others to gain an advantage for yourself is nothing new in nature, but what surprised Catherine Darst was that the copycat frogs were disguising themselves as the less poisonous of the two toxic frog species. Why should they not take the apparently obvious option of looking like the more poisonous variety? To find out, she offered young bird chicks a taste of each type of toxic frog. When the birds ate the more poisonous variety of frog the experience was so unpleasant that it deterred the birds from trying *any* frog for a period subsequently. But when they sampled the less toxic type of frog the birds developed a long-lasting aversion for specifically that type of frog and no other type. So, ingeniously, by imitating the less toxic of the two species, the non-poisonous mimicking frogs gain the much more specific attention of the discerning predator.

Vehicles

To cross a busy road at a sharp bend at the top of a steep hill, what do I do?

Well, you could always try this – although maybe once only, and be sure to carry on you evidence of medical insurance. Mad Japanese inventors have produced a portable zebra crossing to help you out. It is made of plastic painted with black and white stripes, and you simply unravel your 'crossing' at a point that suits you and cross the road. However, the makers do caution that attempting to deploy your crossing on busy roads with no break in the traffic 'might be dangerous'!

Human biology
The senses

Surely it is not possible to judge a person's age by smell?

A study at the Smell and Taste Treatment and Research Foundation, Chicago, has found that the scent of grapefruit on a woman makes her seem to a man to be up to six years younger than she actually is. A man with the same scent leaves no equivalent impression on a woman. Foundation director Alan Hirsch smeared several middle-aged women with an appetising range of plant products, including broccoli, banana, spearmint, grapefruit and lavender, before asking a panel of men to guess their ages. When the women wore grapefruit they were consistently ranked younger than their real ages. The researchers still have no idea why!

Human biology
Heredity

All children are beautiful to their parents – aren't they?

A Canadian researcher who staked out 14 supermarkets to watch how attentive parents were towards their children found that children he subjectively judged to be 'less attractive-looking' were not so likely to be belted into the supermarket trolley, and were allowed to stray much further away from their parents than their prettier, handsomer peers. In other words, they received less care. Dr Andrew Harrell, who carried out the research, says that it is all down to Darwin – we are unconsciously more apt to lavish attention on attractive children simply because they are the most likely to ensure the continuation of our own family!

Medicine
Human biology

Being overweight is medically unwise and socially uncool. Can drugs help?

The French pharmaceutical company Sanofi-Aventis has announced encouraging results of a lengthy trial of a novel anti-appetite drug which works by blocking the brain's natural narcotic-like substances. Nearly half the subjects (44%) who took the drug for a year shed one tenth of their body weight. This promises to help tackle the growing worldwide problem of obesity, particularly in the United States, where more than 60% of the population are overweight or obese.

Domestic events
Food
Physics

Only *you* can make 'perfect' toast – but do even you get it right every time?

Magnetic Design – a company based in Cambridge, England – has developed a device that with the help of a little harmless radiation promises to deliver 'perfect toast every time'. Combining a smoke detector with the heating elements of a toaster, the company's new kitchen must-have can tell automatically when it is time to pop up the perfect slice. But it has no timer, as such. It works by sucking in particles of caramelised bread, which are released as the toast cooks, and blowing them into a stream of radioactive particles similar to those to be found in a smoke detector. The toast particles mop up the radioactive particles, reducing the number picked up by an adjacent sensor. The more singed the toast becomes, the more particles it emits, and the greater the amount of radioactivity that gets mopped up before it can reach the sensor. By setting the toaster to switch off when the radio-activity drops to a certain level – dialled in by you – you can guarantee that your toast will always be cooked to your idea of perfection, no matter how brown you like it, and regardless of whether you start with warm, cold or even frozen bread.

Holography
Computer technology

Can't computer technology enhance our currently rather static holograms?

Researchers from the Massachusetts-based firm Actuality Systems have developed the world's first three-dimensional screen. Shaped like a fair-sized goldfish bowl that the user can physically walk around and view from any angle, the screen faithfully renders images in 3D and in real time. Potential applications include, for example, visualising the relative positions of planes guided by air traffic controllers (which seems an extraordinarily good idea). The system, called Perspecta, works by spinning a circular white polymer disc 15 times per second. Clever computer software chops a 3D computer model into 198 slices which are then projected onto the spinning disc in quick succession, fooling the eye into seeing a solid object hovering in space. At the moment, such images are prone to flicker, but developer Gregg Favalora says they aim to overcome the problem by making the disc spin faster.

Factoid:
'Ants have six legs and when walking move three legs together at a time, keeping the other three on the ground.'

TRUE
They lift three legs together – a front leg and a hind leg on one side of the body, and the middle leg on the opposite side of the body – keeping the other three on the ground.

Physics
Domestic events

But science is always illuminating, isn't it?

US researchers from Vanderbilt University in Nashville, Tennessee, have come up with an efficient successor to the light bulb. Traditional filament lamps waste large amounts of energy, largely as heat. But with the help of some 'quantum dot' nanoparticles, Michael Bowers, Sandra Rosenthal and their colleagues have found a way to mimic the warm white glow of a light bulb that consumes only a fraction of the energy. They have found that tiny crystals containing only 33 or 34 pairs each of cadmium and selenium atoms, when painted onto an ultrabright blue LED (light-emitting diode) give out a warm 'full spectrum' white light, which is very similar to daylight and easy on the eye. This marks a significant step forward for the field of LED technology which, according to the US energy department, could help to cut power usage in the United States (and other Western countries) by about 30%. LEDs last 50 times longer than normal incandescent bulbs, emit twice as much light per watt, produce virtually no heat, and are far more robust than their Edisonian predecessors. Until now, however, getting one to produce a pleasant white light suitable for indoor domestic purposes has been impossible. (Harsher varieties have been available for some years in torches, cycle lamps and outdoor Christmas light decorations.) Hopefully, we can all now look forward to cheaper electricity bills and fewer bulb changes.

Communications

Has anyone thought of a way of making text messages less impersonal?

Russian company SeeStorm can make texting far more visually animated by including a moving image of the text messager. The sender first takes a photo of himself or herself and sends it to SeeStorm. Seestorm uses software to capture the face of the sender and then uses a library of eye and mouth pictures to re-create the speaking movements which are matched appropriately to the words that the caller records as the text message. The texted person then receives an animated version of the caller – complete with moving mouth and lips – speaking the message. The system has become fairly popular on videophones across Asia, Germany, the UK, and North America.

Non-human biology
Electricity

Batman never flew, but will Spiderman ever cling upside-down to the ceiling?

Could be coming closer. A team of US researchers led by Ali Dhinojwala from the University of Akron have managed to artificially recreate in the lab the sticky feet of a gecko. Geckos are renowned for their ability to stick to almost any surface, an effect they achieve by having toes covered in tiny hairs called setae which form electrical bonds with the surface they are walking on, helping them to stick on. The researchers have worked out how to create a carpet of tiny carbon nanotubes with similar properties, but with 200 times the gripping power of a gecko's foot.

Astronomy

Geology

More space geology! But if it's not moondust, is it genuinely stardust?

After a tense wait, on Sunday 15 January 2006 space scientists breathed a collective sigh of relief when it was confirmed that the *Stardust* probe – launched in February 1999 to gather samples from the comet Wild 2, had touched down safely in the Utah desert. But the waiting was not over. Until the probe's collector was opened, no one knew whether it had grabbed anything. Thankfully, the mission has been a huge success, and the principal investigator, Washington University's Donald Brownlee, has calculated that there might be more than a million microscopic specks of dust embedded in the probe's low-density-glass aerogel collecting system. The samples will help researchers to piece together the recipe for the stellar soup from which our solar system formed 4½ billion years ago. Scientists are also inviting the public to muck in and help them dig for the dirt particles by joining the 'stardust@home' project in which home computers help to sift through images of tiny sections of the collector looking for more traces of dust from Wild 2. So far, and surprisingly, a major constituent of the dust has been analysed as olivine – a sort of green sand found on Earth on Hawaiian beaches – although other elements present are the more standard iron, magnesium, calcium, aluminium and titanium.

Palaeontology

Evolution

Did our palaeo-ancestors breathe through their ears?

Scientists studying the fossilised remains of a strange prehistoric fish have found a missing link in the puzzle of where we got our ears from. Martin Brazeau from the University of Uppsala in Sweden has found that *Panderichthys*, which flopped around in shallow water about 370 million years ago and was the immediate predecessor of the first animals to crawl onto land, had modified one of its gills and turned it into an ear canal. The researchers think that the fish initially adapted its gills in this way to produce a primitive snorkel to help it to breathe comfortably in muddy water, or to prevent it from having to lift its head above water to take a mouthful of air. When its descendants later invaded the land, they capitalised on the new design and completed the picture by adding the remaining parts of the ear system we still use today. Evolution is only very rarely frozen in mid-stride by fossils like this, making this a landmark study ... aside from its importance in showing us where we got our ears from.

Factoid:

'Like petrol engines, diesel engines rely on spark plugs to ignite the fuel.'

FALSE

Petrol engines use spark plugs but diesel engines rely on compressing air in the cylinder to make it hot enough to ignite the fuel.

Diseases and disorders
Human biology

Avian flu doesn't spread between humans, but if humans can catch it, why doesn't it?

Researchers in the USA and Japan have solved the mystery of why, when the current strain of avian flu (H5N1) infects a human, it seems to be able to cause disease in that individual but without spreading to other people. The answer lies on the surfaces of the cells in the respiratory tract, a study by Yoshihiro Kawaoka of the University of Tokyo has shown. Human strains of flu recognise sugars on the surfaces of our cells which are linked to each other in what is called a 2,6 configuration. But birds are different and the sugars on their cells are linked in a 2,3 configuration – and so avian flu viruses are adapted to reflect this. When the researchers looked closely at human lungs they found that a certain population of cells called type 2 pneumocytes, which sit in the deepest reaches of the lungs, have the 2,3 sugar linkages more normally seen in birds. This means that when H5N1 infects someone, the infection tends to be confined to this cell population deep in the lungs, rather than growing in the upper airways, which is the usual flu hot spot. This makes it much harder for the virus to escape from the victim in sufficient quantities to infect others. The virus can only begin to spread between humans when it adapts to recognise the normal human sugar configurations.

Solar cell technology
Communications

I'm way out in the country on a sunny day – how do I charge my mobile phone?

Wear a charger. Engineer Joe Hynek from the University of Iowa has come up with a solar-powered handbag and sun hat! The idea is to have about your person the means to provide power capable of charging a mobile phone or powering a laptop. According to Hynek, 'My goal is to use solar cells in a way that's unobtrusive to fashion while making something that's useful.' H'mm, useful it may be, but as for design – unobtrusive it's not.

Electicity
Radioactivity

Radioactivity is the emission of energy: couldn't that energy power a battery?

Researchers in the USA have developed a highly porous form of silicon that can be used to turn low levels of radiation efficiently into electricity. The silicon captures electrons – beta particles – emitted as the radioactive isotope tritium decays, producing useful electricity. Cells based on this principle would be very safe (Rolex watches use tritium on the hands to make them glow in the dark), and would last for long periods of time (over 10 years), making them ideal for hard-to-reach applications such as sensors on remote bridges, weather monitoring stations, and satellites.

Food

The mind

Wasn't it Oscar Wilde who said 'I can resist anything except temptation'?

Cornell University Professor Brian Wansink urges would-be dieters to hide the sweetie jar, or at least move it more than 2 metres (6 feet away). He and his researchers tempted 40 university staff by placing a large jar of chocolates on their desks either next to the staff member, or 2 metres away. Every night the team counted how many treats had been consumed before re-stocking the jars. The results, although predictable, were striking. Hungry participants chomped their way through at least seven chocolates when the jars were right next to them, but only five when the jar was further away. And if an opaque jar was used in place of a clear glass one, the rate of consumption fell by almost half – participants tucked into 4.5 and 3.1 chocolates on average when the coloured glass jars were, respectively, next to them or 2 metres away. 'Not surprisngly,' Wansink points out, 'the less visible and less convenient the candy, the less people thought about it and were tempted.' So the moral of the story is: put the snacks in an opaque box, in a locked cupboard ... and then throw away the key!

Ecology

Communications

But who *wants* a bird's-eye-view of airborne pollution?

Scientists will soon be offering us a bird's-eye-view of pollution when they release a flock of 20 homing pigeons each equipped with a smog-monitoring backpack and a mobile phone. The birds are to take to the skies over San Jose, California, from August 2006 and beam back text messages detailing the pollution they run into as they fly to and fro. The data they collect will be plotted in real time on an interactive map in an Internet blog site ('PigeonBlog'), and cameras carried around their necks mean that the birds will also be sending back aerial photographs of their travels. The project is the brainchild of 'interdisciplinary artist' Professor Beatriz da Costa from the University of California, Irvine, and her two students Cina Hazegh and Kevin Ponto. The team have so far built a prototype system comprising a cellphone circuitboard and SIM card, a GPS receiver to pinpoint each of the birds' positions, and nitrogen dioxide and carbon monoxide sensors to monitor pollution. The next step is to shrink all of the components onto a single circuit-board to make a pigeon pollution-pack for the birds to carry on their travels.

Medical technology
Non-human biology

Humans often have pacemakers fitted. Couldn't animals also benefit?

In September 2004 a team of surgeons from the University of Alabama successfully inserted the first cardiac resynchronisation therapy (CRT) device in a gorilla at Birmingham Zoo, USA. The recipient was Babec, the Zoo's 24-year-old western lowland gorilla, who began to show the symptoms of heart failure in 2003. The CRT inserted into Babec is an advanced form of pacemaker that allows both the right and left sides of the heart to be controlled. According to the Zoo, he is recovering well and beginning to return to some of his typical mannerisms – which presumably means eating a lot of bananas and beating his chest.

Fabric technology
Genetics

Is it possible to reproduce spider-web silk to use for its relative strength?

Chemical synthesis is not economic. But scientists in Israel have artificially produced a form of spider silk which could be used commercially to make protective clothes such as bullet-proof vests, surgical thread, optical fibres and even fishing rods. With researchers from Oxford and Munich, the Jerusalem-based scientists isolated the genes that spiders use to make dragline silk, a form of web which is known for its strength and elasticity. The silk is six times stronger than similarly-sized steel or nylon fibres.

Ecology
Non-human biology

Isn't there some organic way to get rid of an ant infestation?

A newly-identified fungus discovered by scientists in the USA may provide the perfect Trojan horse for getting rid of ant and termite infestations without having to resort to pesticides or chemicals that are dangerous to humans or other animals. Previous attempts to use fungi to wipe out unwanted nests of ants and termites have failed because the ants normally stay well clear of fungi, apparently fully aware that fungal spores can prove lethal to the colony. They even post guards to sniff out and bar from the nest individual ants that have been contaminated by spores. But before it produces any such lethal spores, the newly discovered fungus secretes a substance which ants and termites find irresistible. They collect it and carry it back to the nest, and have even been known to turn it into a bed for the queen. Shortly afterwards, however, the fungus begins to produce spores which infect and kill every member of the nest. Even better, once the nest has been wiped out, the smell of the residual spores deters re-infestation by fresh colonies of insects. Paul Stamets, who made the discovery (in relation to carpenter ants in his home state of Washington) and has now set up a company to commercialise his green means of pest control, is currently screening different strains of the fungus to find specimens which are slower to begin spore production, which would provide sufficient time for nests to become loaded with fungus to ensure the efficient and total destruction of the occupants.

Sport
Domestic events

But surely it is part of fishing expertise to know when your line is about to break?

We've all heard the tale of the one that got away, but that might become a thing of the past if a new line in fishing tackle finds its way onto the market. Researchers Christoph Weder, Brent Crenshaw, and Jill Kunzelman from Case Western Reserve University in Cleveland, Ohio, have come up with a new kind of line that changes colour when it reaches breaking point. It contains a polymer called phenylene vinylene oligomer which glows under ultraviolet light. Healthy line gives off a reddish-brown colour, whereas line that has been damaged by excessive tension, producing a weak spot, glows bright green instead. So just by waving an ultraviolet light over their tackle, anglers would be able to check that everything is in full working order or not. Obviously UV light is not the most convenient way to examine the integrity of a long fishing line, so the team are now exploring ways to produce a polymer with a colour change that is visible in normal light too. They are also looking into ways to use their material as a tamper-proof cover – any damage to the polymer would show up as a green glowing patch.

Factoid:
'Arsenic is a deadly poison: the slightest amount in the human body is fatal.'

FALSE

Actually, the average person's body contains about ten milligrams of arsenic – it is thought to stimulate the production of certain essential body substances. If animals are deprived of tiny levels of arsenic in their diet they will not grow properly. But of course large doses are indeed fatal.

Medical technology
Human biology

How do doctors know where to jab their hypodermics? Mightn't they sometimes miss?

Doctors, paramedics … and vampires … could soon have a new tool at their disposal to help them find suitable veins for taking blood or inserting a drip. Biomedical scientist Herbert Zeman, from the University of Tennessee in Memphis, has unveiled a new device which uses near-infrared light to scan the skin for juicy veins. An image of what the camera sees is then projected back onto the patient's skin, producing a blood vessel 'road map' to guide doctors to the best sites for inserting a drip, or collecting a blood sample. The machine illuminates the skin with an array of near-infrared LEDs, which are clustered around the camera and emit light at a wavelength of 740 nanometres. Light of this wavelength is strongly absorbed by blood but scattered and reflected by other tissues. So blood vessels look dark whereas the surrounding tissues look much brighter. Set up correctly, the new device – about the size of a shoebox – can 'see' up to 8 millimetres (one-third of an inch) into the skin, and pinpoint the position of a vein with an accuracy of one twentieth of a millimetre (0.002 inch). It is likely to prove particularly useful for young children because their veins are often difficult to locate due to their small size and the presence of 'puppy fat'.

Communications

Isn't it the trouble with ring tones that strangers hear them?

If you're looking to spice up your mobile text life, adult film company New Frontier Media might have just the thing for you – not ring tones but ring 'moans'. Fruity users will be able to download a selection of naughty noises said to range from the 'suggestive' to the 'positively tantalising'.

Human biology
Culture

How would you two describe your wedding rings? Gruesome? Grew some?

Royal College of Art jewellery designer Nikki Stott has come up with a highly original concept in wedding bands – a ring grown from the bone of the betrothed! The rings are made with the help of Ian Thompson, a bioengineer at King's College, London. Bone-making cells are harvested from small pieces of the bone of each partner – such as slivers of jaw bone collected when wisdom teeth are extracted. The bone cells, called osteoblasts, are then added to a culture dish where they take over a ring-shaped growth matrix which slowly dissolves as the cells colonise and begin to lay down new bone. When the process is complete, the resulting rough bone circles are then given to the designers who, in consultation with the couple, shape the bone into customised rings.

Medicine

Human biology

The body's nervous system uses electrical activity, but can other body systems use it?

Yes, at least one can. Biomedical scientists in the USA have designed an electric bandage to help promote wound healing. The new product is the brainchild of University of Alabama researcher Dale Feldman and is intended to help promote the healing of injuries including pressure sores ('bedsores') which are a common problem in patients immobilised by spinal injuries, strokes, or old age. The electric bandage applies a current across the wound site and has been shown to significantly increase wound healing rates in patients. Electric fields have been used successfully in the past to stimulate tissue repair, especially in bone: electrical stimulation of a wound site may apparently increase the deposition of collagen – one of the body's primary forms of tissue – which plays a major role in tissue repair.

Factoid:
'Many types of antifreeze are forms of alcohol, yet the antidote for antifreeze poisoning in a human is ... more alcohol.'

TRUE
One way to reverse the effects of methanol poisoning and the glycol in antifreeze is by injecting pure alcohol: methanol, glycol and pure alcohol are all metabolised by the same enzyme in your body, so that the sudden influx of pure alcohol prevents the metabolising of the other harmful versions.

Histology

Human biology

Do laptops leave men all hot and bothered?

A New York-based urologist issued a warning that laptops actually used on top of the lap could be bad for men's sperm counts. Dr Yefim Sheynkin of Stony Brook Hospital studied 29 men in their twenties and thirties and found that using a laptop on the lap for an hour increased the temperature of the average scrotum by over 2.5 degrees Celsius (4.5 degrees Fahrenheit), potentially affecting fertility. Previous studies have found that raising scrotal temperature by as little as 1 degree Celsius (nearly 2 degrees Fahrenheit) is sufficient to affect sperm formation, but the volunteers in the laptop study achieved this rise in temperature after just 15 minutes on the computer. The effects of temperature on sperm formation are well known. A 1999 study showed that American men's sperm production can drop by over 40% during the summer, compared to the winter, and that in hotter temperatures sperm speed drops and the number of defective sperms increases. On the basis of their findings Sheynkin and his team argue that regular daily laptop use could lead to chronically low sperm counts and advise users to put their laptop on a table whenever possible. They are now planning a follow-up study to find out to what extent regular laptop use can affect men's fertility.

Medicine
Diseases and disorders

Many people regard GM products as dubious, but aren't there are potentially great benefits?

Indeed there are. Scientists from Buenos Aires in Argentina, for instance, have created a genetically modified cow which pumps out human growth hormone in her milk. Called Pampa Mansa, the Jersey cow produces over 4 kilograms (almost 9 pounds) of the precious protein a year. She was created by adding the human gene for growth hormone to cow cells in a dish, and then cloning on the modified cells. At her current rate of production, 15 more animals like her would exceed the current world demand for this essential hormone which is prescribed for patients with growth hormone deficiency (of which there are more than 1,000 children needing regular doses in Argentina alone). Originally, patients were treated using hormone extracts obtained from pituitary glands taken from the brains of dead donors, but scares over transmitted diseases, including the degenerative brain disease CJD, have resulted in scientists' switching to using genetically modified bacteria instead. Moreover, the traditional treatment remains very expensive, in Argentina costing a total of more than US $7 million annually. GM cows, on the other hand, capable of producing the protein in a readily-purifiable form in their milk would provide a much cheaper alternative.

Culture
Sport

If you can compete in mind-games online, and gamble online, why shouldn't you hunt online?

An American man with a penchant for shooting things has come up with the world's first website that lets you hunt and shoot real animals on his Texas-based ranch, from the comfort of your home computer keyboard. Visitors can log in to the site and control a gun mounted on a platform overlooking the 135-hectare (330-acre) ranch. Kills are retrieved by an attendant and sent off to the butcher or the taxidermist. John Underwood, the brain behind the site, got the idea after looking at another website in which cameras posted in the wild enable you to snap photos of animals. Texas officials are currently looking into the legality of such a venture. 'Current state statutes don't cover this sort of thing,' says Mike Berger, director of the Texas Parks and Wildlife Department.

Factoid:
'The way people walk is so individual to them that it is possible to identify them solely by their gait on radar-assisted camera.'

TRUE
Researchers at the Georgia Institute of Technology have found that the way you walk is almost as unique as your fingerprint. Indeed, early work on the project has shown that they can positively identify someone 80–95% of the time just by looking at his or her walk. The system – which can use a normal camera but works best with radar – looks at a combination of movements including the arms, legs and torso, and can identify people from up to 180 metres (600 feet) away.

Astronomy

Yet more space geology! But why aim what is effectively a missile at a comet?

In July 2005, at a speed of 23,000 miles an hour (33,000 kilometres per hour), the 820-kilogram (1,800-pound) copper probe *Deep Impact* slammed into comet Tempel 1, opening up a football-field sized crater on the surface of the 10-kilometre (6-mile) long comet, and giving scientists a glimpse of the 4½ billion-year-old material it contains. The collision was monitored from 450 kilometres (300 miles) away by an accompanying parent spacecraft equipped with cameras and spectrophotometers to analyse the composition of the comet. Viewed as icy 'dirt-balls', most comets are essentially flying time capsules dating back billions of years to the time when the solar system was first formed. Locked up inside are pristine samples of the elements and molecules that helped to form us, so blasting a comet apart produces a snapshot of the early solar solar system. During the previous year another probe, called *Stardust*, is thought to have retrieved samples from the surface of comet Wild 2 and is currently en route back to Earth and due to land in 2010. But *Deep Impact* more than merely scratched the surface of Tempel 1, proving that the comet's surface was much more powdery and less compacted than expected – and that although deposits of solid water ice were detected, the quantity of ice was proportionately smaller than expected for the overall size of the comet body.

Light
Plastics
Surgery

Many things respond to different light wavelengths: can we make use of this?

German and American scientists have found out how to make plastics change shape when lights of specific wavelengths (and therefore colours) shine on them. The 'programmed' materials even return to their original shape when exposed to light of a complementary wavelength. The potential number of applications is huge, ranging from staples and paperclips that unlock at the flash of a torch, to tools for minimally invasive surgery such as bloodvessel stents that switch on laser-light command from slender threads to broad cork-screw shapes capable of holding open arteries.

Diseases and disorders
Prosthetics

People recovering from a stroke rely on lengthy therapy: can't robotics help?

Rehabilitation after a stroke usually involves a course of repetitive muscle movements, but the intensity of the rehab makes it time- and labour-intensive. Technologists at Arizona State University have developed a wearable robotic arm dubbed RUPERT – robotic upper extremity repetitive therapy – which aims to take some of the work out of the task. It uses pneumatic muscles at shoulder, elbow and wrist to recreate the right movements to aid recovery.

Diseases and disorders
Genetics
Medicine

Could the monitoring of genes and their products be a means of medical diagnosis?

Scientists at the University of California in Los Angeles have developed a simple, non-invasive saliva test for mouth and throat cancers. The test picks up the products of genes which are normally switched off in healthy tissue but are inappropriately switched on in cancer cells from which they spill into the saliva and can be detected. The team, led by Dr David Wong, compared the saliva of 32 mouth cancer patients with samples collected from healthy individuals of the same age; they were able to pinpoint four genes which were present in the saliva of cancer patients but absent from the mouths of healthy people. These four genes enabled them to pick up 91% of the cancers in the study. But they still missed one cancer in 10, and so they now plan to carry out a bigger trial to track down other genes which can also be used to make the test more accurate. The benefit of this work is that head and neck cancers are often picked up late, by which time the tumour has already spread elsewhere in the body and is therefore much more difficult to treat effectively. A non-invasive saliva test could be used to pick up the condition much earlier, when it is considerably easier to treat and hopefully cure.

Diseases and disorders
Medicine

We know a lot about countering HIV; surely it won't spread so easily again?

Doctors in the USA have uncovered a patient with a highly aggressive multi-drug-resistant strain of HIV capable of triggering AIDS just four months following infection. (Usually it takes 10 to 20 years for the effects to reveal themselves.) The emergence of this strain of the virus is extremely worrying because it can be readily spread to others.

Diseases and disorders
Human biology

Diabetics inject insulin – but isn't there some other way the body could make it?

German scientists have come up with a clever way to deal with diabetes – by pursuading white blood cells to turn into insulin factories. Juvenile-onset diabetes occurs when the immune system mistakenly wipes out the insulin-producing cells of the pancreas. Replacing the pancreatic cells usually doesn't help because the immune system just wipes them out again. But by tricking blood cells into making insulin, recent research on diabetic mice suggests it might be possible to get around the problem.

Communications
Non-human biology

Chimps can be taught sign-language, but might they ever speak?

It's possible that in a way they do already, for a UK researcher has discovered that chimpanzees seem to make sounds to each other that they understand, and that may or may not refer to specific objects. Katie Slocombe, from the University of St Andrews, recorded the grunts produced by two chimps as they sampled bread and apples from two dispensers. She then played the recordings back to another chimp, separately, who spent far more time fishing around the apple dispenser when he heard an 'apple' grunt, and more time poking in the bread dispenser when he heard a 'bread' grunt. That this animal responded similarly to the grunts produced by two different chimps suggests that they are using referential communication. Now, Slocombe plans to repeat the experiment on chimps in a zoo in Leipzig, to confirm whether the grunts refer to specific foods or whether the chimps are simply indicating that they enjoy eating bread more than apples.

Factoid:
'The latest mobile phone accessory is an airbag to protect users who undergo a "facial emergency".'

FALSE
But Ericsson have invented a 'mobile-phone life-jacket' so that people who take their phones on boats will find it harder to lose them overboard. The foam-filled buoyancy packs, which also contain a battery, snap on to the back of the phone in place of the standard battery. If the phone tumbles into the drink, it floats !

Ecology

Why do you think London is called 'the Big Smoke'? And where do you think the smoke is?

Surbjit Kaur and her colleagues at Imperial College, London, have found that the closer you walk to the edge of the kerb, the greater the amount of pollution you are sprayed with. The researchers kitted out 11 volunteers with air sampling devices that sucked in air as they took a 20-minute stroll along London's busy Marylebone Road. When the team analysed the quantity of particulates trapped in the pumps' filters they found that individuals who had walked closest to the edge of the kerb had been exposed to 10% more ultrafine particles than those walking further away, although their carbon monoxide dose remained the same. Fine particles, particularly those produced by diesel engines, have been linked to respiratory problems, cancer and heart disease – so avoid kerb-crawling seems to be the order of the day.

Factoid:
'The sex of a baby is a matter of total chance, determined neither by its mother nor its father.'
FALSE
The sex of a baby is determined by the father's sperm, in which there may be either X or Y chromosomes. If the mother's egg – which carries only an X chromosome – is fertilised by a sperm carrying a Y, the result is a boy!

Diseases and disorders

Medicine

It's nice to know that doctors don't rely on creatures like leeches any more, isn't it?

A team of researchers at Nottingham University, England, led by Professor David Pritchard, is investigating whether the immune-suppressing chemicals pumped out by intestinal worms to prevent them from being expelled from the body can also damp down allergic conditions like asthma. The worms produce eggs which initially hatch into microscopic larvae which can, in a matter of minutes, burrow through skin and enter the bloodstream. The larvae first find their way to the lungs where they each mature into an adult worm over a matter of weeks. They then crawl up to the throat and are swallowed, which carries them to their ideal home, the gut, where they latch on and feed on blood from the intestinal wall. But to prevent the body rejecting its freeloading passenger, the worm pumps out factors that cause the immune system to ignore it ... but with the side effect that symptoms caused by an overactive immune system, such as allergies, also improve. The Nottingham team have now recruited a group of adults with hay fever (an allergic condition) and, after they infect them, will follow them through next spring's pollen season, to see if their symptoms improve. Perhaps it is just as well that it is in any case not particularly difficult to rid the human body of intestinal worms.

Genetics

Non-human biology

Can an insect's sense of smell be more important to it than vision?

Scientists have unearthed the genetic mechanism which enables insects to pick up smells. Without it they cannot detect airborne odours, including that of their next meal – a finding which researchers hope will lead to the development of powerful new insect repellents capable of making humans and crops 'invisible' to mosquitoes and other pests. Leslie Vosshall and colleagues from the Rockefeller University, New York, have found that insects including disease-spreading mosquitoes, plant pests like the corn earworm moth (which damages corn, tomato and cotton), and fruit flies which home in on rotting fruit, all rely on the same gene – known as Or83b – to detect smells. When the researchers removed the gene from laboratory fruit flies, the insects essentially lost their sense of smell. To find out why, the team looked more closely at the insects' antennae – their equivalent of a nose – and found that all of the receptors that enable nerve cells to pick up the presence of an odour were missing. But they came back when the scientists replaced the absent Or83b gene, even if it was the equivalent gene taken from an insect of a different species. The Or83b gene therefore seems to play a key role in ensuring that smell receptors find their way to the correct places on the nerve cells in insect antennae and might prove to be an Achilles heel which can be exploited for the development of novel insect repellents which work by blocking insects' senses of smell. According to Leslie Vosshall, 'If we could use this to interrupt the transport of odorant receptors, we could make mosquitoes "blind" to humans. That in turn would be a good way to prevent disease transmission.'

Histology
Robotics

Are we reaching the point at which 'machines' are made up of organic parts?

You could certainly say so. Researchers in California have developed a self-assembling nanobot (a robot of a miniature size) that 'walks' along powered by heart muscle cells. Jianzhong Xi and colleagues made the tiny micro-machine – which measures just over a tenth of a millimetre and takes steps three-hundredths of a millimetre long – by adding heart muscle cells to a 'backbone' made from a wafer of silicon shaped like a flattened U. Before the muscle cells are added, first a polymer layer and then a gold film are laid down in a specific pattern on top of the silicon. Muscle cells attach well to gold, but not to the polymer, so the pattern of the two can be used to dictate where the cells can latch on. Guided by this pattern, the muscle cells link themselves across the open 'legs' of the U-shaped backbone. Because they have a built-in pacemaker, heart muscle cells automatically contract and relax, opening and closing the 'legs' of the robot and enabling it to walk along. The researchers suggest that in the future, as well as walking around, devices like this could be rigged up as tiny implantable generators which run on glucose picked up from the bloodstream and use piezo-electric materials to power microelectronic circuitry – in other words, the robot's future 'brain', or other implantable electronic devices.

Communications

Impersonal messaging maybe, but could this be the answer for schoolkids and dyslexics?

Texting is a bit impersonal, and it can take ages to tap in the message – but ringing someone could lead to you being sucked into a two-hour long phone conversation and is bound to be more expensive. The answer could have arrived in the form of Voice-SMS, a technology that allows you to send a voicemail message to another phone without running the risk of the owner's answering the phone first. The voice messages can be up to two minutes long and are downloaded directly to the user's phone, so long as they have the correct software. If not, the recipient receives a text message describing how to retrieve the voice message, or alternatively it can be sent as voicemail to an email address. The new technology has been developed by a California-based company who argue that it takes a lot less time and effort to speak a message than to tap out a text.

Factoid:

'H. S. Richardson, son of the inventor of Vick (Vick's VapoRub™), the cold remedy, in 1907 renamed the product after his own brother-in-law, Victor Richardson.'

FALSE

He named it after his brother-in-law Joshua Vick. (A man very rarely has the same surname as his brother-in-law, you know.) But it was undoubtedly an improvement on 'Richardson's Croup and Pneumonia Cure Salve' and remains popular all over the world. In Britain alone 2½ million jars of 'Vick' menthol ointment are sold every year.

Astronomy

Astro-geology

How is it possible that scientific specimens end up as coffee-table conversation pieces?

Meteorites are the latest fashionable must-have, it seems. Some private collectors are willing to shell out up to US $9,000 a gram – that's 5,000 times the price of the equivalent weight in gold – to own one. The surging price is fuelling the meteorite equivalent of a gold rush as prospectors head for the locations such as the remote Sahara and Gobi deserts and Patagonia, where the arid conditions preserve specimens for millions of years. The unfortunate spin-off is that scientists are getting priced out of the market, which means that precious specimens dating from the birth of our solar system, or the early history of Mars, are being lost to research and instead ending up on people's bookcases. To combat the problem scientists at the University of Arizona, armed with $200,000, have set up the 'Southwest Meteorite Center' to buy up samples before they disappear into private collections. The centre will also analyse and authenticate meteorites for collectors in return for a small sample. The specimens they accumulate will be stored in a climate-controlled facility to prevent further chemical deterioration, and made available to scientists on request.

Computer technology

Is the number of microcircuits on a chip like the number of angels on a pin-head?

Conventional computer chip-making technology is now reaching the limit of how many microcircuits (transistors) can be packed onto a chip. To solve the problem the researchers are attempting to borrow from biology by using natural materials like DNA and proteins, which have a pre-programmed structure, to arrange the distribution of nanoparticles on a silicon chip. This will potentially shrink processing to the scale of individual molecules, greatly increasing the speed and power of computing.

Light

Doesn't sound-sensitive lighting seem a good idea for *the day after* a boozy party?

South Korean company Daejin Digital Micro Products have come up with a light bulb that changes colour with the beat of the music, and produces very little heat, helping to keep clubbers looking and feeling cool. The new system uses an array of six ultrabright LEDs which plug into a standard 12-volt halogen light fitting – but unlike the halogen alteranative, they do not get hot. The six LEDs are wired to a built-in audio sensor that controls their colour. Bass tones produce a blue light, mid ranges trigger green, and trebles provoke a red colour. They can also be switched to a continous cool white colour. Unfortunately, with each lamp currently costing over US $35, clubs are unlikely to be dancing to Daejin's doors to buy a set quite yet.

Histology
Medicine

Without eyes or other senses, how do bacteria know what and when to attack?

Scientists have found that bacteria use a sonar-like system to spot other cells around themselves in order to target them for destruction. This finding explains how some bacteria seem to 'know' when to switch on the production of certain toxins designed to break open nearby cells, including other micro-organisms, in order to release useful nutrients, to help the bug spread, and to ward off attack from the immune system. Working on an intestinal bug called *Enterococcus*, Michael Gilmore and his team at Harvard in the USA have found that the bacterium releases two chemicals into the environment. One of the two substances sticks on to foreign cells, while the second substance reports back to the bug, telling it to make the toxin. But if there are no cells near by, the first substance sticks to the second and prevents it from reporting back, and so no toxins are made. The scientists say that the discovery will help to design new treatments to combat bacterial infections by designing toxin-inhibitors, which will be particularly useful for tackling antibiotic-resistant bugs. The researchers also hope that it might possible to tame certain bacteria and engineer the system so that it can be used to detect other things in the environment, such as minerals, or other disease-causing bugs.

Forensic science
DNA profiling

Burglars who wear gloves leave other traces if they raid the fridge too, don't they?

Inviting colleagues to a free buffet, DNA fingerprint expert Heather Zarsky had an ulterior motive. She asked diners to sample a range of foods, leaving what they didn't want. From the leftovers she extracted complete DNA profiles of nearly half the diners, and partial profiles from a further third. The aim of the work was to work out what foodstuffs preserve the best evidence of peckish burglars. Apparently, housebreakers can't resist raiding the fridge and abandoning their spoils half-eaten – providing the police with valuable clues to the identity of the perpetrator ... but only if they know what foods to home in on. Now they do: apples, cheese, carrots and pizza. Hungry would-be burglars are therefore advised to eschew these items in favour of chocolate – which proved useless at identifying a snacker!

Factoid:
'A jug of hot water placed in the freezer turns to ice more quickly than an identical jug of cold water.'
FALSE
Hot water will always take longer to freeze than water which starts cold – but it is true that the hot water will begin by losing proportionately more heat more quickly, a fact that has led to this common assumption.

Non-human biology
Medicine

Wouldn't it be nice to sleep all winter? Mightn't it be *useful*?

Japanese researchers have uncovered the chemical switch that controls an animal's hibernation pattern, a finding which might hold the key to triggering similar states of suspended animation in humans. To discover the hibernation trigger, Noriaki Kondo and colleagues of the Mitsubishi Kagaku Institute of Life Sciences in Tokyo studied a large group of chipmunks. They found that the levels of a protein in the blood called hibernation-specific protein (HP) changed in accordance with when the animals hibernated, and showed an annual cyclical change in levels. HP dropped just before the animals went to sleep, and remained low throughout their hibernation. When they woke up again, the levels rose again. But in the fluid surrounding the brain, the opposite was true, and when the animals went to sleep, HP levels rose. And when the researchers mopped up the HP in the brain with a dose of antibodies the animals were prevented from nodding off. Now it remains to find out exactly how the hormone works, and whether the same effects might be possible in humans. After all, if humans can be put into a similar state, it might be possible to reduce tissue damage caused by strokes, heart attacks and surgery, by simulating the extremely low metabolic demands of hibernating tissues.

Laser technology
Human biology

Wouldn't lasers be too dangerous to use as stun-guns for crowd control?

Researchers working for the US military are developing a laser stun-gun capable of inflicting paralysis and excruciating pain on anyone unlucky enough to be within its 2-kilometre (1,900-yard) range. The new weapon, known as a 'pulsed energy projectile' or PEP, is being touted as a crowd-control measure to 'neutralise' rioters, and could be in action by 2007. It emits a powerful laser beam which generates a charged plasma cloud whenever it hits someone. The expanding plasma over-excites the nervous system triggering severe pain sensations, and temporary paralysis. At the moment the researchers are working on ways to optimise the system so that it is even more effective at producing pain but without damaging healthy tissue. However, some pain experts around the world are horrified and have expressed concerns over the long-term effects of such a weapon, which could include life-long pain syndromes that might be triggered if the stun-gun causes the nervous system to 're-wire' itself.

Factoid:
'Because bones have to be strong, they must also be heavy – they account for at least one quarter of the body's total weight.'

FALSE
They actually account for slightly more than half of one quarter – about 14% – and a little more in men than in women.

Domestic events
Ecology

The washtub's spin cycle is the best way to start drying clothes, isn't it?

Yes, but even the effect of spinning can be improved on. Dinesh Shah and Daniel Carter at the University of Florida have found that clothes remain wet after a wash because the tiny gaps between the strands of a fabric act like capillary tubes, tightly holding on to water by surface tension. But by researching a detergent and softener cocktail that locks onto the fabric and breaks down water surface tension, the two have been able to pursuade even the most stubborn fabrics to shed 20% more water during the spin cycle than they would normally – the clothes are helping to dry themselves 20% more quickly – using less energy in the process.

Human biology
Sociology

Adults can usually avoid passive smoking – but children may not. Does it matter?

Research suggests that passive smoking can 'prime' a child's brain for nicotine, making it more prone to addiction later. Margaret Becklake from McGill University in Montreal recruited almost 200 nine-year-old boys and girls, testing their lung capacities and their saliva for nicotine breakdown products, and logging their parents' smoking habits. Four years later she followed up with the same children. Those who had had the highest levels of nicotine breakdown products in their saliva (indicating greater exposure to passive smoking) were twice as likely to have become smokers.

Diseases and disorders
Medicine

Why is that allergies have become so prevalent in humans over the last 20 years?

Perhaps we are getting closer to an answer. Scientists at the University of Michigan have found further evidence that friendly bacteria in the intestine play an important role in preventing allergic conditions, including asthma. Killing them off with antibiotics, they say, might be partly responsible for the surge in allergies over the last 20 years. So how can bacteria down in the stomach and intestines affect the sensitivity of the airways higher in the body? This is how: anything that is breathed in ultimately ends up being swallowed because mucus produced in the lungs traps inhaled particles and then wafts them up to the throat from where they proceed down into the stomach. In the intestines the immune system learns to recognise whether a substance is dangerous or not, and to ignore, or tolerate, harmless substances. The success of this process depends upon the microorganisms known as the flora which inhabit the intestines. If the balance of gut micro-organisms is upset by antibiotics, a change of diet, or switching from breast-milk to formula feeds, then the tolerance process can break down, triggering allergies. The researchers believe that exposure to certain allergens, including mould spores or pollens, at the same time as the body's gut flora are altered, can result in the development of an allergy to that substance. Their suggestion – try to eat a healthy diet packed with fruit and vegetables, especially after a course of antibiotics, to help maintain a thriving population of intestinal micro-organisms.

Non-human biology

Horses 'left-' or 'right-*handed*'? You're talking fetlocks again, aren't you?

Knowing whether a horse is right- or left-handed might help you to beat the bookies in future, according to Irish researchers from the University of Limerick. Riders and trainers often report that their mounts respond better when turning or jumping in one direction or the other, but whether this is down to training or to an underlying innate cause has until now remained unknown. To find out, Jack Murphy and his team studied 40 untrained horses destined to become showjumpers or dressage competitors. They watched which leg the animals preferred to use when stepping forward, and which direction they chose when detouring around obstacles or rolling over on the floor. The researchers found that females preferred the right side, whereas male horses preferred their left. About 10% of all horses showed no preference. Because a well-balanced mount is the most desirable for riding and racing, these results could help trainers and jockeys to develop their mounts' weak sides. Meanwhile, however, knowing a horse's preferred side could help punters better predict the horse's competition performance, because the direction and bends in a race will evidently suit some runners better than others. Bad news for the bookies!

Ecology

Pollution control

So a hope that once looked for-lawn is actually achieving reality?

In a bid to clean up its act in time for the 2008 Olympics, China's choking capital city, which has seen traffic on its roads rising by 15% per year, has taken to planting grass on roofs to help filter the air. Most major capital cities rely on oases of green open spaces planted with trees and vegetation to preserve air quality. But Beijing is too crowded for any more green belts, so officials are turning to rooftops instead. In 2004 they planted 10,000 square metres of evergreen grass on rooftop lawns, and in 2005 the target was 100,000. They are also intending to shift 200 of the worst polluting factories. By the end of 2004 officials claimed to have reached their initial target of 227 days with clean air ... although many are sceptical about the standards used to make the claim.

Factoid:
'Beards are bad for your health.'

TRUE
Men who shave regularly are healthier and have sex more often than their hairier counterparts, a study has shown. Researchers at the University of Bristol found that men who shave at least once a day are more likely to be married, have better jobs, and are less likely to smoke, whereas bearded men in addition have a 70% higher chance of suffering a stroke.

Medicine
Diseases and disorders

Is it possible to detect deteriorating brain function before behavioural symptoms appear?

A new study has shown that measuring people's brainwaves might hold the key to predicting who is at risk of developing dementia over the next ten years. US researchers Leslie Prichep and Roy John from the New York University Medical School followed up a group of 44 men and women who were aged between 64 and 79 and, tests showed, had normal brain function at the time they joined the study. On several occasions over the following seven to ten years the volunteers had their brainwaves measured non-invasively using a technique known as an electroencephalogram (EEG). By the end of the study, 27 of the patients had developed signs of dementia, and by looking back at their earlier brainwave measurements on these patients, the researchers were able to pinpoint characteristic changes in brain activity which occurred before the patients developed outward signs of cognitive decline. In particular, the researchers noted, there was an increase in a pattern of brain activity known as theta waves, and a loss of synchronisation between the brain's two cerebral hemispheres. These results suggest that it might be possible to use this technique to screen for individuals at risk of dementia.

Forensic science
Human biology

So the stomach finds something indigestible in telling a lie?

Forget polygraph tests to flush out a liar, criminals could soon be given away by their stomachs, according to research carried out at the University of Texas by Pankaj Pasricha and his colleagues. The team gave 16 volunteers an electrogastrogram (EGG), a measurement of the nerve activity in the stomach. The subjects were asked to lie about some things, and tell the truth about others. Intriguingly, their stomach nerve activity shot up whenever they told a lie but remained unchanged when they were honest – evidence, says Pasricha, 'that the gut has a mind of its own'.

Solar technology

Wouldn't it be nice to be able to find things in your handbag at *any* time?

Anyone who has spent ages rummaging around in a handbag for her keys on a dark evening, usually in the rain, will appreciate a new self-illuminating solar-powered handbag designed by Brunel University's Rosanna Kilfedder. Powered by an internal battery, the bag's electroluminescent lining glows whenever the zip is opened, showing you what's inside, and switches off again after 15 seconds to prevent the battery going flat if the bag is left open by accident. On sunny days the external solar panels help to recharge the battery, which can also be used to run a mobile phone, or even a portable music player. Dubbed Sun Trap, the design could soon be available to the general public.

Non-human biology
Sound

Surely we should be grateful to any frog who ensures that we can't hear his croaking?

US researcher Albert Feng and his colleagues have found that a species of Chinese frog that lives in a noisy environment has evolved a clever way to prevent its croaks being drowned out by the sound of nearby running water – it croaks in ultrasound. The researchers discovered the strange vocal habits of the male concave-eared torrent frog (*Amolops tormotus*), which lives in a mountainous region of China, by accident when they used sensitive recording equipment to monitor the frogs' activity. As well as croaking the conventional way, these frogs were also producing very high-pitched noises (up to 34 kilohertz), inaudible to humans. When the researchers recorded the sounds and played them back to captive (male) frogs, they found that their study subjects croaked in unison with the recording. To find out how the frogs were responding to the ultrasound the researchers then temporarily blocked up their ears, instantly stopping the karaoke. Feng and his team believe that the sounds are a mating call designed to cut through the loud noises of running water which are prevalent in the frogs' aquatic environment. They are now eager to track down some females to see how (or, indeed, if) they respond to an ultrasonic 'ribbit'.

Medicine

Surgery

Robotics

After the advent of keyhole surgery, have people lost interest in micro-robot surgeons?

Not exactly. In fact, scientists at the University of Nebraska Medical Center in Omaha, USA, have developed a tiny robotic surgeon which can wander around inside the body, providing doctors with a minimally invasive look at what they need to see, or performing minor surgical or biopsy tasks. Dmitry Oleynikov and his team's tiny device, which is only 15 millimetres (three-fifths of an inch) across, consists of two rotating aluminium cylinders linked by a thick axle bearing a camera. A spiral tread pattern on the cylinders enables them to grip the walls of the abdominal cavity to move around, and it is controlled by a joystick. The team have used the robot to assist them in removing a pig's gallbladder, and have explored the abdomen of a live pig, driving the robot down the pig's interior through a small incision in the stomach wall. The benefit, of course, is that such an intervention requires no other, larger, external incisions, so avoiding unsightly scars. In addition, more than one robot can be passsed through the same small incision, either independently to explore a wider area or together to provide different angles of vision for the controlling surgeons. Clever and potentially useful as the process may be, however, it has been criticised as not constituting enough of an advance on existing surgical techniques for patient or surgeon.

Genetics
Sociology

Has it ever been proved that dyslexia may have a genetic cause?

Jeffrey Gruen and his team from Yale University have pinpointed a gene that causes dyslexia. The researchers screened the genes of 536 subjects from 153 families with a history of dyslexia, and homed in on a region of chromosome 6 where they found that a piece of DNA had gone missing. The affected gene, DCDC2, is normally switched on in parts of the brain that are involved in reading and language processing. It is assumed that as the nervous system builds during gestation, some nerve cells fail to migrate to the correct position.

Genetics
Diseases and disorders

How can knowing the genetic make-up of dogs help to diagnose human disorders?

Eric Lander and his colleagues from MIT have published the most complete genetic sequence to date of the dog. Significantly, dogs exhibit an enormous range of physical and behavioural traits – in particular, susceptibilities to certain diseases, to which the genome sequence will enable researchers to pinpoint underlying genetic causes. And because humans suffer many of the same diseases as dogs, tracking down the combinations of genes that make dogs sick will also highlight the causes in humans. So once again, dogs have proved that they are man's best friend.

Ecology
Electricity

Isn't the main problem with wave power the conversion to electricity in large amounts?

A UK-based engineer, Ed Spooner, has come up with a more efficient way to generate electricity from wave power. His solution is a clever seabed-mounted device, dubbed the snapper, which turns the ponderous slow movement of ocean swells into a succession of rapid movements ideal for electricity production. The snapper comprises a floating buoy tethered to a mobile central armature within the generator on the seabed. As the buoy rises and falls on passing waves it draws the armature, containing a series of fixed magnets, up and down past a series of coils in the base unit. This movement induces pulses of electrical current in the wire. But to produce the rapid movements required to generate electricity efficiently, a second set of fixed magnets in the base unit, aligned with the magnets on the armature, hold the armature in place until the rising buoy generates enough upward thrust to pull the magnets apart and allow the armature to move up to the next set of magnets which are placed vertically above the first. As the buoy continues to rise this action is repeated several times. When the armature reaches the top of its travel, and the buoy begins to fall down the wave, a spring returns the armature to the starting position, again as a series of short sharp movements. This process turns what would otherwise be a gentle up-and-down motion into a succession of swift electricity-generating jerks. A prototype of the invention, which was presented at the World Maritime Technology Conference in London, shows that the system produces increased current-generating forces compared with existing technologies and might therefore enable current wave-generating systems to be made smaller, cheaper and more efficient.

Non-human biology

But birds don't usually notice how different the cuckoo's egg is, do they?

Researchers have come to understand how the African village weaverbird (*Ploceus cucullatus*) prevents itself being taken for a ride by cuckoos – it's all down to the speckles on the eggs. David Lahti and his colleagues at the University of Massachusetts have described how village weaverbirds lay clutches of eggs which all show a very similar pattern of speckles, suggesting that if a cuckoo laid an egg in the nest, the bird will be able to spot the imposter almost immediately. But when the researchers studied two colonies of the birds that had been introduced more than 200 years ago to two islands without any cuckoos, they found that those birds' eggs no longer exhibited the same speckle patterns. In a neat demonstration of the power of evolution, these results show how, in the absence of pressure from parasitic cuckoos, the appearance of the eggs has altered because having a similar pattern is no longer so much of an advantage.

> *Factoid:*
> 'It is a scientific fact that a facility for storytelling may be inherited.'
>
> **TRUE**
> A certain substance found in the brain and known under the abbreviated term BDNF has two variant forms called 'met' and 'val'; one of its main functions has to do with long-term memory. People with the val form are better at recalling stories, whereas people with the met form are more susceptible to the effects of ageing, depression and Alzheimer's.

Diseases and disorders
Medicine

Stem cell therapy focuses on repairing or replacing damaged tissue – even of the heart?

Scientists at Johns Hopkins University in Baltimore, Maryland, have announced that stem cell therapy can be used effectively to treat heart damage caused by heart attacks (known as myocardial infarcts) in pigs, paving the way for using the same technique in humans. The scientists injected each pig with about 200 million mesenchymal stem cells collected from the bone marrow of other adult pigs. The injections, which covered an area of the heart wall about the size of a small coin, were placed directly into a region of heart muscle recently damaged by an infarct, by threading a small catheter into the heart via an artery. A second 'control' group of pigs received placebo injections lacking any stem cells. The pigs were then monitored for two months. The pigs that received placebo injections became much worse and developed congestive heart failure. But those that had received the stem cell injections showed full recovery of heart function and their hearts contained virtually no signs of 'scarring', a cardinal signature of previous heart attacks. In such scars muscle tissue is replaced by stiff fibrous tissue which cannot contract properly, reducing the heart's pumping ability, and the scar itself can also affect the electrical properties of the heart, sometimes triggering rhythm disturbances and cardiac arrest. Pigs provide a useful comparison with humans because their organs and physiology are very similar to our own. These encouraging findings suggest that this technique may work effectively in humans.

Communications

What happens if you want to send a message that is urgent, informal, happy *and* excited?

A new voicemail system developed by scientists at the Massachussets Institute of Technology can label messages as urgent, not urgent, formal, informal, happy, sad, excited, or calm, just by analysing the caller's tone of voice. Named Emotive Alert, the system, designed by Zeynep Inanoglu and Ron Caneel, studies the volume, pitch and speed rate from the first 10 seconds of each message and compares the results with eight stored 'acoustic fingerprints' representative of the eight message types. The system then labels the message type accordingly and sends the recipient a text message emoticon corresponding to the message type. The acoustic fingerprints were produced by feeding hundreds of voice messages, which had been grouped into each of the different categories, into a computer learning package to pick out the features they all had in common. In tests so far the system can tell happy from sad and excited from calm, but finds formal versus informal and urgent versus non-urgent more difficult to tell apart. This is probably because formality and urgency tend to be conveyed more in the wording, which the machine does not analyse, rather than the sound, which it does. However, the researchers are hoping to produce a more personalised version, tailored to an individual's most frequent callers.

Palaeontology
Bacteria

Movies are full of dinosaurs and mammoths that thaw out and live – why doesn't it happen?

NASA scientists working on samples of Alaskan permafrost have discovered a form of life that has been frozen in time for over 30,000 years. When the scientists thawed the ice under a microscope the newly-identified organisms, bacteria now called *Carnobacterium pleistocenium*, showed signs of life and began swimming around. They date back to an era when mammoths and sabre-toothed tigers roamed the Earth, and were collected from a tunnel drilled through the ice near the town of Fox. Richard Hoover, who made the discovery, says that the findings raise the prospects of finding life on Mars because the bacteria were extracted from half-metre-(20-inch-) thick wedges of ice similar to structures seen on the red planet. Indeed, the *Mars Express* probe has revealed the presence of a giant frozen sea near the Martian equator, which could provide ideal conditions for microbial activity.

Factoid:
'The symptoms of the common cold are caused always and only by virus infection, so antibiotics do not help at all.'

FALSE
Virus infection certainly causes the vast majority of colds, but some of the symptoms in some cases may be produced by secondary infection by bacterial agents – in which case, antibiotics can help – or by allergic sensitivity or even a dramatic change in environmental temperature or air quality.

Computer technology
Genetics

Computer technology will soon have to go organic – but how?

A US researcher has found a way to perform the DNA equivalent of origami, paving the way for the construction of complex nano-scale structures, including the next generation of microchips. Paul Rothemund, from the California Institute of Technology, uses a piece of single-stranded DNA made up of 7,000 DNA 'letters' which he folds, rather like a piece of modelling wire, using additional short pieces of DNA called oligonucleotides. These oligonucleotides lock onto a unique 'address' on the DNA strand, and when they bind they staple the DNA into the correct shape. By linking other nanoparticles to the oligonucleotides, like a molecular cargo, they can be used to position more molecules with great precision, including potentially the components required to assemble nano-scale circuits and computer chips. This is a key area of exploration by the microprocessor industry who, within the next 10 years, face 'red wall' – a point at which, using present techniques, it will become impossible to make computer chips any more powerful.

Non-human biology
Instinctual behaviour

Nature v nurture – but at puberty, doesn't nature always win?

Researchers from Switzerland and the USA have found that puberty plays a big role in the songs sung by canaries. By playing a song very different from the normal song pattern of a canary to a group of young birds, the researchers were able to teach the birds to sing in an entirely new way. But when the birds reached an age coinciding with the avian equivalent of puberty, the canaries promptly ditched the song their keepers had taught them and reverted to a singing style much more reminiscent of their species.

Human biology
Heredity

Genes pass on family characteristics – but what ensures that we are individual too?

Among all the myriad genes in the genome are 'mobile elements' corresponding to pieces of DNA that may 'jump' into another gene and affect its function. They may reduce the other gene's operation or alternatively boost it. Scientists have now proved that at least one of these jumping genes is active in the developing human nervous system, and can affect what sorts of brain cells are produced as the brain grows. This is why even the brains of identical twins turn out differently, and if you cloned yourself, your human replica would also differ from you!

Diseases and disorders
Medicine

Which is worse here – the condition or the treatment?

Researchers have stumbled upon a possible new treatment for the inflammatory intestinal condition Crohn's disease – a dose of worms! The immune systems of patients with Crohn's are thought to be over-reacting to the 'good' bacteria in the intestine, producing painful and recurrent inflammation, ulceration, weight loss and intestinal obstruction. The disease tends to be much more common in the developed world than in the Third world, where most people carry intestinal parasites such as worms, and this has led doctors to speculate that worms in some way help to damp down the immune response in the gut. So, over a six-month period doctors gave 29 volunteers with Crohn's disease regular doses of the eggs of a species of worm called *Trichuris suis*, which normally infects pigs. After 12 weeks of worm therapy, 19 of the patients were completely free of Crohn's symptoms. By the end of the study, 80% of the patients had responded to the therapy, and 73% had gone into remission and were symptom-free. No one in the study developed any side effects. The benefit of using pig worms is that once they hatch, the worms remain in the bowel without invading other parts of the body, and the eggs do not pose a threat to other people because they must be incubated in soil for at least a week before they can colonise another person. The authors suggest that the worms are producing factors which help to suppress the over-activity of the immune system in the bowel, and that worm therapy might be a simple alternative, or even addition, to Crohn's therapy in future.

Food

The senses

But how would the chef feel if a critic said the menu tasted nicer than the food?

Most people expect just to look at the menu in a restaurant, but thanks to chef Homaru Cantu, owner of restaurant Moto, now you can literally taste it too! That's because he has come up a concoction of vegetables dyes that can be used to replace the ink in an ink-jet printer. Replace the paper with soybean or starch sheets and you have, quite literally, an edible menu. As the sheets roll off the printer Cantu covers them with a mixture of flavourings and then fries, freezes or bakes the results. Diners at his restaurant are also invited to spice up their food by tearing strips off the menu and adding them to their meal. The new invention ushers in the possibility of edible adverts in magazines or newspapers, where readers are not only treated to the image of a new a pizza or new crisp brand – they can taste them too. And the magic doesn't stop there. Cantu also has plans to cook steak, and even bread, 'inside out' using a laser, producing steaks that are seared in the centre but raw on the outside, and loaves that are crusty in the middle! So it may not be long before you can go into a restaurant and order something you like the lick of!

Diseases and disorders

Are there any physical symptoms that might show a predisposition towards mental illness?

Researchers in Australia have found that your nose – or rather, its ability to correctly identify certain smells – could hold the key to detecting people who are at risk of mental illness. We've known for some time that people with schizophrenia are unable to correctly recognize smells – they might identify the smell of pizza as 'orange', or of bubblegum as 'smoke'. But no one knew what came first – whether the schizophrenia was causing the difficulty in identifying smells, or the other way round. By studying a group of people who were at high risk of developing mental illness, Warrick Brewer and Christos Pantelis from the University of Melbourne found that all of the patients who went on to develop schizophrenia displayed the inability to correctly identify smells *before* they showed any other symptoms of schizophrenia. 'An accurate and reliable diagnostic tool for schizophrenia could allow for early treatment or prevention and minimise the extensive and significant distress to those in the community directly and indirectly affected,' says Brewer.

Factoid:
'Camels' humps can hold up to 15 litres [just over 3 UK gallons; just under 4 US gallons] of water.'
FALSE
Camels' humps don't actually hold *any* water – they store fat which they can use to sustain themselves when food is scarce. And camels can go a long time without drinking any water at all.

Histology
Human biology

We've all heard the 'science bit' in cosmetic ads, but do skin cells really age?

Researchers in New York have found that rather than just losing their natural elasticity as we get older, skin cells actually do become more rigid, contributing to the ageing effect. The reason, say the researchers, is because the cytoskeleton, the 'scaffolding' that holds the cells together, becomes more rigid in older cells. But the good news is that there are drugs that can weaken the cytoskeleton, which might therefore make excellent anti-wrinkle creams and which the research team is now testing.

Medicine
Food

Olive oil is said to be good for you – but does it have any real medicinal benefit?

Researcher Paul Breslin and his colleagues from the Monell Chemical Senses Center and the Universities of Pennsylvania and Philadelphia have found that top-range olive oil is as good as a dose of ibuprofen, possibly explaining the beneficial effects of the so-called Mediterranean diet. The team tracked down a component of the oil called oleocanthal which, like ibuprofen, blocks the action of an enzyme called cyclooxygenase, involved in inflammation. About 50 millilitres (3 tablespoons) of olive oil is equivalent to a standard dose of aspirin, which may explain why people who eat an olive-oil-rich diet traditionally have lower levels of heart disease and stroke.

Chemistry
Palaeo-botany

Petrified wood? Yeah, fine. But what's it petrified *of*?

US researchers have found a way to achieve in days what takes nature millions of years – creating petrified wood, which, say the inventors, could hold the key to more efficient industrial catalysts, filters and clean-ups. That's because petrified wood is very hard but also very porous, with a large internal surface area, making it ideal for soaking up or separating substances, or acting as a catalytic converter. Wood naturally becomes petrified (turned to stone) when it is buried in an oxygen-poor soil that prevents it from breaking down. Slowly, over millions of years, the organic material is replaced by minerals, such as silicates, which are soaked up from the surrounding soil. To speed up the process, the research team from the Pacific Northwest National Laboratory took blocks of wood, gave them an acid bath, then soaked them in a silica solution for a few days to saturate the wood with minerals. They then baked the wood at 1,400° Celsius (2,550°F) in an argon furnace designed to exclude oxygen. The result was a new silicon carbide which, according to research scientist Yongsoon Shin, exactly replicates petrified wood. The researchers have now focused their efforts on trying to produce narrower, highly ordered pores in the new silicon carbide in order to boost its industrial potential.

Food and drink
The mind

Look – I'll just have another drink, and perhaps you'll explain it all to me again ...?

Alcohol has been used by humans for medicinal and recreational purposes for thousands of years, but scientists still don't know how it makes us tipsy. To tackle the problem, researchers in the USA studied a family of rats which have a tendency to be highly sensitive to the effects of alcohol. These rats carry an altered version of a gene that codes for a receptor used by brain cells to detect an inhibitory nerve-transmitter universally known as GABA (because it is a lot easier to say than 'gamma-aminobutyric acid'). The researchers tested the electrical activity of the rats' brains and found that giving them alcohol made their nerve cells much more sensitive to the inhibitory (depressant) effects of the GABA neuro-transmitter compared with normal rats, possibly explaining why alcohol makes people sleepy, lethargic, and uncoordinated. When the rats were given behavioural tests after drinking small amounts of alcohol (producing a blood-alcohol level below the drink-drive limit in most countries) they became very uncoordinated, compared with normal rats given the same amount to drink. These results suggest that alcohol produces its intoxicating effects by interfering with the brain's inhibitory neuro-transmitter systems. They might help to identify individuals who are at risk of alcohol-related problems, or might possibly contribute to strategies to reverse drunkenness.

Non-human biology

How does one ant tell if another ant is from the same nest or is a 'foreigner'?

Biologists have known for some time that ants who are all members of the same nest exude an identical cocktail of volatile substances called cuticular hydrocarbons, enabling them to recognise each other, but how their antennae facilitated that recognition was something of a mystery. Now, researcher Mamiko Ozaki has pinpointed a specialised sensory structure, called a sensillum, located on the antennae, which sounds the alert when things don't smell right! The sensillum is a tiny tube about 0.02 millimetre long and about 0.004 millimetre in diameter, and it houses a large number of chemically-sensitive nerve fibres (up to 200). By painstakingly recording the activity in the nerve fibres from the sensillum, Ozaki found that they fired off nerve impulses only when he exposed them to smells of 'foreign' (non-nestmate) ants. Cleverly, the nerves which would normally respond to the smells of nest-mates were deactivated, sorting friend from foe.

Factoid:
'The average person's brain weighs 500 grams [just over 1 pound].'

FALSE
The human brain weighs up to three times that amount – between 1.2 and 1.5 kilograms (2¼ and 3 pounds) – and men's brains are generally slightly heavier than women's.

Astronomy

Are we so attractive to this asteroid that it keeps coming back?

Space enthusiasts will be treated to the Earth's closest encounter yet with a passing asteroid, which will be visible from the ground as it buzzes the Earth, passing inside the orbit of some of our satellites. Scientists first spotted the 300-metre (1,000-foot) wide NEO, or near-Earth object, which they called 2004 MN4, hurtling towards us in June of 2004. Initially, it was thought to be on a collision course with us, but subsequent observations – specifically, measurements taken in December 2004 – have enabled scientists to refine the course and eliminate the possibility of a direct impact either with us or with the moon. Instead, they think it will pass us by at a distance of 36,350 kilometres (22,600 miles) from the Earth's centre, just below the altitude of our geostationary satellites, and will appear visible to the naked eye to people in Europe, Africa and western Asia, as a fast-moving star passing through the constellation of Cancer. Slightly worryingly, it is due to arrive on the 13th of the month (let's hope that's not a Friday!) ... but fortunately not until April 2029. And if it does hit us? Scientists are confident that if an asteroid of this size collided with Earth, it would cause local devastation and regional damage, but wouldn't be expected to cause any sort of global disruption. Bear that in mind, together with the knowledge that 2004 MN4 (more technically known now as 99942 Apophis) is due to return just as closely – if not even more closely – in 2036 and 2069.

Plant biology
Histology

How many other plants do you know with lightning reactions?

Charles Darwin called the Venus flytrap (*Dionaea muscipula*) one of the most wonderful things in the world – yet more than 150 years later researchers are still struggling to explain how the plant closes its trap so quickly. But now we think we know the answer. Previously, scientists had suggested that the rapid closure of the trap occurs when special 'motor cells' deflate, rather like a balloon popping, which brings the two halves of the leaf together. But even this would not account for the speed with which the process takes place. To solve the problem a team of researchers in France, the USA and the UK used high-speed photography, capable of capturing 400 frames a second, to track what happens during the tenth of a second the trap takes to close. The photos have revealed that the flytrap 'snaps' from a convex shape to a concave shape very quickly, just like a broken tennis ball turned inside out that can rapidly be 'popped' from one stable shape to another. This is achieved by the arrangement of cells and fibres within the wall of the leaf – although precisely how the arrival of a potential meal inside the trap triggers the shape change, the scientists haven't yet worked out.

Electricity

How many viruses do you know that are actually useful?

Angela Belcher and her colleagues at the Massachusetts Institute of Technology have used a virus to help them make a better battery! The virus was one called M13, which consists of a long, thin spiral of protein surrounding a straight piece of DNA. By genetically modifying the virus to add some additional chemical groups to the helical protein, and then bathing the particles in cobalt oxide and gold, the researchers were able to produce high-efficiency electrodes which improved the performance of a lithium battery to twice that achievable with conventional electrodes made of carbon.

Surgery

Now, how could I ever have thought a hip replacement was a sort of flask?

Biomedical engineers at Leeds University, England, have designed a new kind of hip replacement which, they claim, should last longer than present designs. Most current artificial hips have a metal head which plugs into a metal socket. The continuous metal-on-metal rubbing action grinds away small metal particles that are toxic to the bone which anchors the artificial joint in place, making it work loose. The Leeds team have therefore come up with a prosthesis comprising a ceramic head inserted into a metal socket. The new device produces far less metal debris, which means it should last longer than existing hip replacements.

Electricity

What did the mobile phone say to the pad? 'How much are you going to charge me?'

The days of hunting around for the correct charger, and disentangling leads for phones, PDAs, cameras or camcorders, could soon be over thanks to a novel solution from a company based in Cambridge, England, called Splashpower. Based on the same principle that powers cordless electric toothbrushes, the new invention comprises a charging 'pad', similar in size to a computer mouse mat. To recharge something, you simply lay it on the mat. Better still, the system will top up as many electrical items as you can fit on the mat surface at once. It works by using a coil, housed in the mat, to transfer power magnetically to smaller chewing-gum-sized coils built into the gadgets you want to charge up. Thankfully, the inventors have taken steps to ensure that the magnetic field will not erase nearby bank cards or videotapes, should you inadvertently attempt to charge those too. They are currently seeking licensing deals with companies that make handheld devices, like Nokia and Palm, and optimistically predict that we could be seeing the first 'drop-and-charge' devices on sale before the end of 2006.

The senses
Histology

Will advances in gene therapy make a difference to the treatment of the deaf?

Researchers in the USA have found a gene which might hold the key to regenerating the delicate hair-like cells in the inner ear which make make hearing possible and cause deafness when they are damaged. Zheng-Yi Chen and colleagues from the Massachusetts General Hospital began by pinpointing all the genes that are active in the ear of a developing embryo. One of the genes they spotted, called called Rb1, the retinoblastoma gene, seemed to switch off the production of the crucial hair cells, presumably when the right number had been made. Under normal circumstances these hair cells pick up the vibrations made by sound waves hitting the eardrum and turn them into electrical signals that the brain can understand. But as we age, or if we are exposed to loud noises over long periods of time, numbers of hair cells decline and are not replaced, causing deafness. But when the researchers cultured cells that had been altered to lack the Rb1 gene, they found that the cells divided, producing many new hair cells. If they then added the Rb1 gene, the production of new cells stopped. This suggests that if a way could be found to temporarily switch off the Rb1 gene in the ears of people with hearing problems, it might be possible for them to develop new hair cells to replace the ones they have lost, restoring their hearing. Unfortunately, the Rb1 gene is known as a tumour-suppressor. It stops cells growing out of control and if damaged can cause cancer. So the researchers would have to find a very precise way to temporarily switch off the gene in just the right cell types, or they might trigger tumour formation.

Ultrasound technology
Medicine

Ultrasound is used to monitor pregnancy. Surely it has other medical applications?

Dr Who may have his sonic screwdriver, but researchers from the University of Pittsburgh have come up with an 'ultrasound flashlight' that should help medical staff pinpoint veins and other structures beneath the skin more easily. Traditional ultrasound involves placing a probe onto the skin and then looking at an image on a computer screen next to the patient. This can make it difficult to relate what's on the screen to where something is located on the body. But the new system uses a probe equipped with a screen that projects what it is seeing onto a two-way mirror above. Looking through the mirror above the probe the user then sees a roadmap of what's beneath the skin apparently projected onto the skin surface. Medical students and nurses learning to insert intravenous cannulae were much more successful in their attempts to hit veins when they tested the system. Let's hope it finds its way into the surgery soon!

Factoid:
'Owls can rotate their heads all the way round – a full 360 degrees.'

FALSE
They can only turn their heads through 270 degrees – but that's still three-quarters of a full turn!

Astronomy

What could a star have done to be thrown out of its own galaxy?

Astronomers have spotted a star, which they are dubbing 'the outcast', leaving the Milky Way galaxy. The first of its type ever seen, it is travelling so fast – over 2.5 million kilometres per hour (about 1½ million miles per hour) – that scientists think that it was lobbed out by a massive black hole sitting at the Galaxy's centre, that it is the surviving member of a binary system which twirled around each other close to the rim of the black hole, and that one of the pair was swallowed, but the survivor was flung out, slingshot-style, towards the edge of the Galaxy. It is now about 180,000 light years away from the Earth.

Human biology
Medicine

Stem cells are useful for repairing tissue damage – but even in the heart?

A veterinary team has been able to use growth factor injections to kick-start stem cell repair of areas of a dog's heart damaged by a heart attack. Until now such a result had been shown only in mice and rats, which are not representative of humans. Dogs are a much better model, and the therapy suggests that the same approach may be feasible in us. Moreover, the researchers stress that injection of growth factors into the heart is a minimally invasive procedure, and persuading the patient's own stem cells to carry out the repair gets around the potential problem of tissue rejection.

Fabrics

Physics

Shall I go green today, or turn yellow? Or do I feel blue?

University of Connecticut researchers have come up with a new weavable polymer that changes colour at the flick of a switch, ushering in a new range of theoretically knittable and washable textiles that will be able to alter their colour or pattern to suit the wearer's needs or mood. Just as in a normal fabric, Professor Greg Sotzing's 'electrochromic' polymers contain electrons which soak up lights of different wavelengths to give the material its colour. But when an electrical current is applied, the energy levels of these electrons can be altered so that they absorb light of different wavelengths, altering the colour of the strand. By stitching the threads into a garment, and linking them with microscopic wires to a controller unit, the criss-crossing strands can create the fabric equivalent of a TV screen, dividing the material into a series of small coloured pixels. And by hooking the controller up to a camera capable of imaging the surroundings, the garment could quite literally blend you into the background, like a form of camouflage. The team make the new polymer by spraying it out of an electrically-charged nozzle. As soon as the threads leave the nozzle the solvent in which they are dissolved evaporates, and the individual strands plait themselves together like a piece of rope. At this stage the researchers then chemically bond carbon and sulphur groups to the strands before adding an oxidant which cross-links them together. It is this latter process which gives the strands their colour and electrochromic behaviour. But don't rush out expecting to buy your chameleon suit quite yet because there are still a few problems that have to be ironed out. At present, for instance, the colour range remains distinctly limited.

Non-human biology
Histology

Pheromones are chemical messengers – but exactly how is the message transmitted?

Researchers at the University of Texas have pieced together the workings of insect pheromones – the chemical signals that these animals use to attract mates, and that control colonising and feeding behaviour. Insects pick up the presence of pheromones with their antennae, but exactly how the antennae detect and react to pheromones was poorly understood. It turns out, according to Dean Smith and his team, that that these chemical messengers work rather like professional socialites on a matchmaking mission at a cocktail party. When pheromones bump into an insect's antenna they latch onto a locally-produced substance called an olfactory binding protein (OPB) (one of which is appropriately named LUSH), and thrust it into the arms of a waiting receptor on a nerve cell near by, exciting the nerve fibre and triggering a behavioural change. The scientists hope that by developing chemicals that can interfere with this process it may be possible to produce 'baits' to attract insect pests into traps, which would help to control the spread of diseases like malaria, or repellents to prevent people from being bitten in the first place.

Medicine

Isn't it the very diversity of the dangers that makes dressing wounds so problematical?

Scientists in the USA have come up with a new wound dressing that can simultaneously help to control bleeding and stop infection, saving vital minutes on the battlefield and potentially making the difference between life and death. Martin Bide and Matthew Phaneuf have based their new material on a polyester that gives it elasticity and that is impregnated with the blood-clotting protein thrombin and with a broad-spectrum antibiotic called ciprofloxacin. When applied to a wound the thrombin activates the blood's clotting system, helping to control bleeding much more rapidly, while the antibiotic leaches out into the tissue to mop up infection. The inventors hope that the speed with which the material can be used to control bleeding would free soldiers' hands to deal with other life-and-death issues. Off the battlefield there are many other applications for this sort of advanced wound dressing, including use by explorers, climbers, or people hiking in remote areas.

Factoid:
'The average person's heart pumps about 5 litres (1.1 UK gallon; 1.6 US gallon) of blood a minute.'

TRUE
Although this figure can increase to between 25 and 30 litres (i.e. by five or six times) a minute during exercise.

Ecology
Non-human biology
Plant biology

Why is it that nobody and nothing seems to *like* caterpillars?

US researchers have uncovered a new form of plant defence which deters hungry caterpillars by giving them a fatal dose of indigestion. Penn State University's Dawn Luthe and her colleagues made the finding by studying insect-resistant strains of maize (corn). They found that these plants produce an enzyme called maize insect resistance cysteine protease (Mir1-CP). Plants armed with this defence switch it on as soon as a caterpillar begins to eat. Once the enzyme gets inside the animal, the Mir1-CP attacks a structure called the peritrophic matrix, punching holes in it. This matrix is a mucous membrane that assists with the absorption of nutrients in the intestines of insects, and it also helps to keep out parasites and potential infecting micro-organisms. When damaged by the plant protein the matrix becomes riddled with holes, rendering the affected caterpillar liable to infection and unable to absorb its food very effectively, thus also stunting its growth. Indeed, when the researchers tested caterpillars fed maize cells that had been programmed to express Mir1-CP, they found that it retarded their growth by up to 70%. The team suggest that producing GM crops which express this protein could have significant implications for cheap and effective ways to control insect pests globally.

Non-human biology

Back-scratching is not a luxury but essential social interactivity, isn't it?

Chimpanzees, like humans, know how to direct each other to hit the right spot during a back scratch, it seems. Previously only humans were thought to use gestures to direct the behaviour of others, because to do so requires the recipient to be able to infer the signaller's meaning – an ability linked to cognitive capacity. But now Simone Pika, from the University of St Andrews, together with John Mitani from the University of Michigan, have found evidence that, at least when it comes to a back rub, wild chimps can do it too. The researchers watched male chimpanzees grooming each other in the Kimbale National Park, Uganda. To direct a grooming partner to pay more attention to a neglected area, the chimp being groomed would scratch a certain spot on itself in an obvious and exaggerated manner. Most of the time the groomer would promptly start paying attention to precisely the spot the gesturer had just indicated. This form of referential communication, such as pointing to something in the environment with the expectation of a specific response from another, say the researchers, had previously been considered beyond the capability of non-human primates in the wild.

Diseases and disorders

How long does it normally take to complete an AIDS test?

Researchers from Cornell University and the University of Albany, led by biophysicist James Turner, have described how they developed a prototype handheld device that can perform a rapid AIDS test. The gadget contains an array of electrodes coated with antibodies that recognise CD4, a surface marker found on the white blood cells targeted by HIV. When a drop of blood is added to the device, the antibodies lock on to any CD4 cells, altering the electrical properties of the electrodes. On the basis of the change in electrical activity the machine can predict how many cells are present and therefore whether a person is likely to need anti-HIV drugs.

Non-human biology

Isn't an ant who makes life easier for other ants an antihero?

Researchers at the University of Sheffield have discovered a chemical 'no-entry sign' which ants erect to keep their nest-mates on the right track. Previously it was thought that ants used only attractive signals to point the way to the best places to eat, but Elva Robinson and her colleagues have described how, while investigating these attractive signals, they accidentally stumbled upon the ant equivalent of a road-closed sign. The ants use these signals to improve their foraging efficiency by preventing nest-mates from making fruitless detours.

Computer technology
Physics

But a high-resolution image surely needs more power, not less?

Most people will have noticed the revolution in computer screen technology that has seen large space-hungry desktop monitors replaced with slim-line liquid-crystal display (LCD) models. LCD screens don't just save space, they save power too and produce far less heat, which also cuts down the need for air conditioning in busy offices. Yet even though they can offer resolutions of 1,600 by 1,200 pixels, the image is still not up to the quality you get from a glossy magazine. But now technologists at manufacturer Hewlett-Packard have come up with a new kind of LCD which, they say, can yield resolutions of 7,000 by 5,000 pixels and can also be scaled up to billboard size for roadside or city advertising. LCD works by applying electricity to crystals sandwiched between polarising filters which operate a bit like sunglasses. When the current flows, the crystals change their shape, altering the polarity of the light passing through them and making the pixel 'switch on'. But to keep each pixel active, electricity must be continuously supplied. The new screens only need power to *change* their image. The inventors have found that when liquid crystals are placed in contact with tiny polymer 'posts', they naturally arrange themselves around the post in either a flat or a tilted orientation. Applying electricity to the crystals causes them to flip from the horizontal position to the tilted one or vice versa. But both positions are stable, so when the power is switched off, the crystals remain where they are and any displayed image is preserved. Each of the polymer 'posts' is smaller than one-thousandth of a millimetre, so that several thousand of them can fit into the space of one pixel on a standard LCD screen, producing vastly superior resolution.

Food
The senses

Could a liking for fatty foods really be genetically derived?

The French are well known for their fat-soaked cuisine so it may be logical that a group of researchers from Dijon should have discovered a unique taste bud for fats. Philippe Besnard and his colleagues at the University of Bourgogne in Dijon have pinpointed a receptor on the tongues of mice which is called CD36 and seems to make fatty things taste nice to these animals. Given a choice between water tainted with a fatty substance, and plain water, normal mice prefer the lipid-spiked drink. But when the team used genetic techniques to nullify the CD36 gene from another group of mice, the animals' preference for the fatty drink disappeared. The researchers suspect that humans also have CD36 receptors and that variations in their sensitivity might be connected to eating disorders and obesity. Intriguingly, in the mice, when fats lock on this receptor it also triggered changes in the intestine, including the release of bile in preparation for digesting a fatty meal, even before they had swallowed a mouthful.

Factoid:
'The human eye blinks an average of one million times a year.'
FALSE
In fact, a person blinks 4.2 million times a year on average.

Diseases and disorders
Medicine

Can't someone come up with an effective vaccine against cervical cancer?

Someone has. A vaccine called AS04, targeting human papilloma virus (HPV) – the agent that causes cervical cancer – has now been shown to provide long-term protection against the disease. The vaccine consists of the shell of the virus and primes the immune system to produce antibodies capable of neutralising two of the highest-risk forms of the virus (types 16 and 18) before they can gain a toe-hold in the susceptible tissue in the cervix and then trigger cancer. Although the vaccine had previously been shown to produce strong immunity when first administered, it was not clear how long this protective effect might last. To find out, Diane Harper and her team at the Dartmouth Medical School, USA, followed up a group of 776 women who were given either the active vaccine or a placebo nearly five years before. Amongst the women who received the active vaccine there was evidence of strong immunity to papilloma viruses types 16 and 18 (those represented in the vaccine), and it was 100% effective at preventing long-term (over 12 months) infection and pre-cancerous changes in the cervix associated with these two forms of the virus. The vaccine also cross-protected against disease related to other forms of HPV and was extremely safe. Cervical cancer is the leading cause of death amongst women worldwide, largely because it is so common in the Third world. These results show that this vaccine will undoubtedly make a huge impact on women's health worldwide, but especially in less developed countries that lack the infrastructure to deliver a screening programme.

Genetics
Physics

How can we get bacteria to be even more useful to us?

Chris Voigt and his colleagues at the University of California have produced the bacterial equivalent of a camera. The team added a gene similar to the one used in our own eyes to detect light, and coupled this light-sensing apparatus to a second gene to make the bacteria change colour whenever they were illuminated. Although this result is merely a proof of principle, Chris Voigt points out that the system could readily be altered to make the light-sensitive bacteria produce a useful product – such as forms of plastic – so that very accurate structures could be formed, at the resolution of a single bacterium, at the flick of a switch (and light-bulb).

Non-human biology

Stem cell therapy can be just as beneficial for animals as for humans, can't it?

Researchers at the Royal Veterinary College in England have found that stem cell therapy can help racehorses to recover from injuries more quickly. They have described how, compared with conventional treatments of rest and gentle rehabilitation, when bone marrow stem cells collected from a horse's sternum were multiplied in a laboratory dish and then injected into an injured tendon, they triggered much more rapid healing in the damaged tissue, a more rapid return to the racecourse, and fewer injuries subsequently.

Medicine

Food

Do drugs as an aid to dieting really work?

It's a well-known phenomenon amongst cannabis users that the drug boosts appetite. That is because the hypothalamus, the part of the brain which sits above the roof of the mouth and, appropriately enough, controls feelings of hunger, is sensitive to cannabinoids, the active substances present in marijuana. Nerve cells in the hypothalamus have CB1 receptors, which are rather like docking-stations for marijuana-like chemicals, including a substance called anadamide, which are produced naturally in the brain. When these chemicals lock on to the receptors, they instruct the nerve cell to trigger hunger pangs. The French company Sanofi-Aventis has now come up with a drug called Rimonabant (Acomplia) that can block these receptors, suppressing appetite, and promote weight loss. In a recent trial involving over 1,500 significantly obese Europeans, those given the highest dose of the drug lost about 8 kilograms (17½ pounds) in weight over a two-year period. Encouragingly, the study subjects also showed a 27% increase in their levels of 'good' cholesterol, although only 50% of it could be explained on the basis of their weight loss, suggesting that Rimonabant might also have a beneficial effect on blood cholesterol levels and could therefore be useful for patients with diabetes. However, the amount of weight loss was fairly modest, and there were side effects of the treatment including nausea, diarrhoea, and vertigo, but the company have high hopes for the successful marketing of the drug worldwide both as a dieting aid and as an aid to quitting smoking.

Ageing

So it should be 'old mens sana in corpore sano'?

Dutch researchers have found that exercise makes a signifi-cant impact on brainpower amongst the elderly. Boukje van Gelder and colleagues looked at data collected from 295 men born between 1900 and 1920, and followed up their levels of physical activity, including walking, cycling, gardening or other odd jobs, and cognitive function for the ten years from 1990 to 2000. Men who dropped their level of physical activity showed a 3½-fold greater drop in brainpower than men who remained active; men who increased their exercise levels showed no decline in their abilities. The researchers suggest that their study shows that keeping active in old age also helps the brain to remain fit, probably by boosting blood flow and stimulating the birth of new nerve cells in the hippocampus, the part of the brain concerned with forming new memories.

Factoid:
'At the age of five, virtually all children are able to repeat nursery rhymes, brush their own hair and teeth, do up and undo buttons, and blow their nose.'

FALSE
Fewer than 40% of children at the age of five are sufficiently co-ordinated to blow their noses – most either forget to close their mouth or do not squeeze their nose at the right time. The majority just give up and use their sleeves, according to a survey; the same study also found that the only skill more difficult to master is tying shoelaces, which most children do not manage until they are six.

Physics
The senses

Is it just our eyes, or why do some creatures' ideas of camouflage seem so conspicuous?

Researchers from Bristol, England, have confirmed why some animals' choices of 'camouflage' actually involve the use of highly conspicuous colours and markings – it is for the same reason that military camouflage uses strongly contrasting colours, because the colour-clashes help to break up the outline of objects, making them harder to recognise. The Bristol team cut moth-shaped triangles of card, with a worm for the edible 'body', and pinned them to trees. If the body disappeared they assumed that a bird had spotted the moth and turned it into lunch. The decoy moths were camouflaged with a pattern designed to resemble the oak tree bark to which they were fixed. The researchers tested patterns containing either strongly contrasting colours, or less contrasting colours. They also compared the difference between patterns which reached the edge of the wings, and hence disrupted the surface outline, and those which did not touch the edge. Exactly as the theory predicts, moths decorated with the most striking colours that reached the edges of the wings were found least often by birds. Following the theory, however, zebras should be practically invisible.

Diseases and disorders
Histology

Perhaps instead of a 'rivet gun', you would rather I spoke of a spigot and a cask?

Scientists at the University of Geneva in Switzerland have discovered a bacterial toxin equipped with its own 'rivet gun' to help it punch holes in cell membranes. One of the ways that bacteria cause disease is by poking holes in the walls of our cells and then soaking up the nutrients that flood out through the puncture. But while studying one of these toxins, called aerolysin, Gisou van der Groot noticed that it has a very unusual mechanism of anchoring itself to the target cell. The researchers identified a small fatty region at the tip of the toxin molecule which, when driven through a cell's membrane, abruptly changes its shape as soon as it hits the watery cell interior, and bends over into a hook. Seven of the toxin molecules all link together in a circle, just like a rivet. They form a pore through which the cell contents can leak out into the jaws of the hungry bacterium lurking outside. A comparison with other bacterial toxins shows that they too seem to be resorting to this rivet-like action, potentially highlighting a novel avenue by which scientists might combat bacterial infections.

Histology
Medicine

But how, and for how long, does stem cell therapy benefit the heart?

Scientists at the University of Texas have helped to shed light on how stem cells can help to repair damaged hearts. Edward Yeh and his colleagues injected human stem cells into mice with heart disease and used their 'human fingerprint' to track where the cells went. They found that some of the stem cells turned into muscle and linked up with the mouse's own heart muscle cells, essentially wiring themselves into the heartbeat, while others turned into specialised cells capable of producing new blood vessels. The researchers also found that the stem cells were still working in the mouse heart a year after they were injected – which is a long time in the lifetime of a mouse.

Non-human biology

Does competition when mating cause any creature to resort to disguise?

Researchers studying the giant Australian cuttlefish have found that males of the species often successfully resort to the marine equivalent of cross-dressing to father offspring. During the mating season, fertile females are usually jealously guarded by large males, preventing smaller males from getting a look in. So the smaller animals often disguise themselves as females, by changing colour and arranging their tentacles in a more feminine fashion, in order to slip past the male consorts lurking near by. Two out of three of such matings apparently result in successful fertilisation.

Diseases and disorders
Medicine

Can spectral analysis (as used forensically) be used medically to identify organisms?

A team of scientists led by Professor Luis Garcia-Rubio from the University of South Florida has developed a miniaturised sensor that can non-invasively pick up the presence of infectious diseases using as little as a single drop of liquid. The new biosensors recognise the characteristic 'fingerprint' spectrum produced when light shines on different microbes. Because different organisms absorb and scatter light differently, the pattern produced when a sample is analysed can be compared with a catalogue of known infections to identify the bugs that are present. The sensors, which can be used to analyse blood samples or to check the purity of drinking water, are capable of picking up the parasites that cause malaria, the virus that causes dengue fever, common bacterial causes of intestinal infections and dysentery including *Salmonella*, *E. coli*, *Shigella* and *Cryptosporidium*. It can also identify anthrax, making the system attractive to anti-terrorism squads. Once a sample is placed on the sensor, the data is transmitted wirelessly to a remote location for analysis, meaning that the system, which is currently undergoing field trials, is highly portable. The inventors hope that it will help to tackle the problem of waterborne illnesses which claim 2 million lives each year, most of them children, due to the fact that only one-sixth of the world's population have access to clean water. Rapid diagnosis of pathogenic illnesses could also help to stem the spread of diseases following environmental disasters such as tsunamis and earthquakes.

Non-human biology
The senses

Would you care how you stank, so long as it was offensive to mosquitoes?

Why is it that some people are eaten alive by mosquitoes, whereas others escape unscathed? It might be because, to a mosquito at least, some of us smell better than others. Suspecting that some individuals might produce natural mosquito repellents, researchers in Rothamsted Research in Harpenden, England, first identified groups of people whom mosquitoes seem to avoid. They then collected samples of 'total body odour' from each person, enabling them to home in on 11 key chemicals which have the strongest mosquito-repelling action. To isolate the smells the scientists used a Y-shaped piece of apparatus which gives mosquitoes the option of flying towards or away from different odours present in the arms of the Y. At the same time, working with scientists in Denmark, they have also found a substance produced by some cows, called 6-methyl-5-heptene-2-one, which wards off flies from around the herd. The research team are now in the process of patenting the chemical compounds they have uncovered, with the aim of using them to produce more effective mosquito-repellent sprays and lotions.

Diseases and disorders
Laser technology

Some polymers react to laser light – can this be made use of medically?

US researchers have developed a laser-activated corkscrew that can be threaded into blood clots which have blocked arteries, and used to remove them. The system relies on what are called shape-memory polymers or SMPs, which can revert to a pre-programmed shape when laser light of the correct wavelength shines upon them. Duncan Maitland and his colleagues from the Lawrence Livermore National Laboratory in California have described how, using a model of the carotid artery in the neck, their thin polymer, which is initially straight, can be used to penetrate a blood clot which has blocked an artery. A quick blast of laser light locally then transforms the polymer to its corkscrew shape, enabling it to snare the offending blood clot which can then be withdrawn from the blocked artery, restoring blood flow. At the moment doctors often use clot-busting therapies to dissolve obstructions, but these can be costly and carry a high risk of subsequent bleeding. The Livermore team hope that their approach will provide a cheaper and more effective alternative which may be usable in a larger number of patients and carry fewer side effects.

Factoid:
'Human children have more bones than human adults.'

TRUE
Children have 300 bones, but as they grow, some of the bones fuse together, resulting in a total of only 206 in adults.

Astronomy

There's not much we don't know about the planets of the solar system, is there?

Well, there's even less, now that we have some idea of the length of a Saturnian 'day'. Measuring the length of a day on Saturn – in other words, how fast the gas-giant is turning – has always been a problem for space scientists. As NASA researcher Giacomo Giampieri puts it, 'It's like trying to tell whether an unmarked CD is spinning in the CD player: without some kind of marking on the surface – like a label – you can't tell.' And that has been the difficulty. You just cannot tell by eye how rapidly an amorphous lump of gas is rotating. But now researchers think they have cracked the problem. The answer is 10 hours and 47 minutes, and it will help scientists to model more accurately how Saturn formed in the first place, and how it comes to have the biggest equatorial bulge around its middle of all the planets in the solar system. So how did they arrive at that answer? The *Cassini* probe, which is in orbit around the planet, has provided the clue. Since its arrival off Saturn in July 2004 the probe has been making readings of Saturn's magenetic field. By analysing this data the team were able to pinpoint a small but regular signature – a blip – in the magnetic field. By measuring how frequently the blip cropped up, the researchers have deduced the spin rate of Saturn.

Ecology
Physics

Oh, come *on!* What is the possible point of a sea wall that has holes in it?

German manufacturing giant BASF has developed a new way to protect sea walls from the incessant abuse of the sea – by coating them with a thick surface that has holes in it. But there is method in this madness. The spray-on treatment, which is currently being tested against the ravages of the North Sea on the Danish island of Sylt, is administered by mixing two chemicals, an isocyanate and a polyol. The polyurethane mixture cures (hardens) in 20 minutes, making it perfect for use between tides. A high-pressure spray applies the mixture to stone surfaces, or it can be mixed with loose stones and sprayed in layers up to 30 centimetres (1 foot) thick. But it is not a solid layer. The surface is punctuated with large pores a few centimetres (an inch or three) across. When a wave slams into the surface, some of the energy is dissipated by the natural elasticity of the material. But even more is mopped up by the pores as sea water tries to force its way through, turning destructive wave energy into heat and noise. According to project leader Marcus Leberfinger, a wall reinforced with the coating has 'reliably withstood the huge impact of the waves during this past storm season'. Apparently the porous plastic is also proving popular with wildlife, the holes making ideal homes for crabs, limpets and shore plants.

Medicine

How can you be given a complete course of injections all at once?

Like this. The system, which has been developed at Ghent University in Belgium, involves packaging the substance to be delivered inside tiny capsules which are also pre-loaded with a water-absorbing molecule called dextrin. The drug capsules are then injected under the surface of the skin. Over time, water oozes into the capsules and dissolves links in the dextrins, causing them to swell, which eventually pops the capsule and discharges the drug contents. The time it takes each capsule to burst open can be controlled by altering the number of links in the dextrins. The team suggests that the invention could be useful for people living in the developing world where frequent visits to a doctor are impractical.

Drugs and drug abuse

There are plenty of organic methods to rid Colombia of coca plants, aren't there?

There certainly are, and one of the latest strategies to wipe out the country's associated cocaine industry is by unleashing an army of hungry caterpillars. It is proposed to breed thousands of *Eloria noyesi* moths, natural Andean inhabitants, and release them into the main coca-growing areas where they will make straight for the coca plants and lay eggs all over the leaves. Within a week the eggs will hatch into caterpillars that will devour the foliage, destroying the plant. The Colombian government is currently considering the proposal, but has turned down such ideas in the past on environmental grounds.

Diseases and disorders
Laser technology

A major problem with anti-cancer drugs is to deliver them to a specific site, isn't it?

Scientists in Australia have developed minute nanocapsules which can be used to deliver anti-cancer drugs to tumours, sparing other healthy tissue from side effects. The capsules, which measure about 1 micron – or one thousandth of a millimetre – across can be coated with an antibody which directs them from the bloodstream to a tumour. Once they are in the tumour, a quick blast with a harmless skin-penetrating laser producing near-infrared light causes the capsules to open up, discharging their contents. To make them, Frank Caruso and his team from the University of Melbourne, Australia, have engineered a polymer which they add to a suspension of drug particles so that the polymer forms a sphere enclosing the drug, several layers thick. They then add tiny gold particles 6 nanometres – 6 millionths of a milli-metre – across, which stick onto the surface of the polymer, rather like the speckles on a bird's egg. It's these gold particles which are sensitive to the laser light and allow the capsules to deploy their drug cargo at the desired time. When near-infrared light hits the gold spots, they instantaneously melt, rupturing the capsule, but without harming the contents. The outermost layer of the nanocapsules consists of a fatty (lipid) layer to which a variety of antibodies can be attached to help target the capsules to specific tumours. So far they have tested the technique using a simple enzyme called lysozyme without any loss of activity from the enzyme when it was released from the capsule. The next step for Caruso and his team is to shrink the nanocapsules even further, and then test whether they can safely be administered to a living creature.

Evolution

The mind

Hasn't it always been better to understand things ape-*riori* than ape-*osteriori*?

Scientists in Germany have found that the ability to plan ahead is not, as originally believed, peculiar to humans. In fact, our great ape relatives, including those distantly related to us, the orang-utans, seem to be able to do it too, proving that one of our most formidable mental abilities must have evolved early in our ancestry. Nicholas Mulcahy and Josep Call of the Leipzig Max Planck Institute have shown that both bonobos, which split away from humans about 7 million years ago, and orang-utans, which split off about 14 million years ago, are capable of picking up the correct selection of tools they might need to solve a future problem. The researchers showed the animals an apparatus which required them to use a specific tool to retrieve a food or drink reward. Later the animals were placed in a different room with a selection of tools, one of which could be used to perform the task they had been shown previously. At this time they had the chance to pick up any tools they wanted. They were thereafter moved to a waiting-room outside for between 5 minutes and 14 hours, and then allowed into the room containing the apparatus. If they had the right tool they could obtain their reward. These results show that the apes selected, transported and saved a tool not because they immediately needed it, but because they had a good notion they would need it in future. This is very strong evidence to prove that saving for a rainy day is not a uniquely human activity and to contradict the suggestion that such behaviour only arose in hominids over the last 2½ million years.

Food

Ecology

So a future household may have a 'meat-maker' as well as a 'bread-maker'?

Scientists from the USA and the Netherlands have come up with two new ways to produce edible cultured meat in the laboratory. The first approach is to grow the cells on thin membranes in large flat sheets, stretching the tissue as it grows. The flat sheets could be stacked up to increase the overall thickness of the 'meat' product. The other approach is to grow the cells on small beads that expand considerably with just small increases in temperature enabling the beads to be enlarged to accomodate the product as it grows. The mature cells can then be harvested and turned into a processed meat, rather like nuggets or hamburgers. The scientists point out that there are several important benefits to the technology, including reduced levels of artery-clogging fats, 'meats' that are vegetarian-friendly, and reduced emissions of greenhouse gases associated with rearing livestock.

Factoid:

'Microsoft Research are looking into ways to implement foot-pedals to help you control your desktop.'

TRUE

At the moment the organisation is looking at which aspects of the mouse and keyboard control of the Microsoft Office package could be best translated to pedal power. This is likely to be welcomed by sufferers of repetitive strain injury affecting the wrist – but might it lead instead to an outbreak of 'driver's ankle'?

Diseases and disorders
Laser technology

Chemotherapy for leukaemia may leave a young boy infertile – can anything be done?

Unlike adult men, many young boys who develop leukaemias go on to make a full recovery with appropriate therapy. But the therapy destroys the 'germ' cells which produce sperm in the testes, rendering the patient infertile. Recently, working with mice, scientists devised a method of removing these germ cells before therapy, and then re-injecting them afterwards to restore fertility. However, the germ cell samples were often contaminated with leukaemic cell 'stowaways' which triggered fresh disease when the germ cells were reimplanted. Now, though, Japanese researchers have found a way around the problem – by using a special technique called FACS (fluorescence-activated cell sorting). This system uses a laser beam to sort cells into different groups according to colour-coded markers. Starting with germ cell samples from mice with leukaemia, the Japanese scientists added markers designed to identify rogue white blood cells. The machine was told to pick out only the germ cells, and these were then implanted into mice which had previously been sterilised by chemotherapy. These mice regained their fertility. When the germ cell samples were not sorted by the FACS machine, but implanted directly into recipient mice, all of them developed leukaemia. Clearly, further tests will be required to determine the safety of this method, but these results are encouraging and suggest that it may soon be possible to restore fertility to boys rendered infertile through chemotherapy.

Food and drink
The senses

Why do you keep thrusting excuses to drink red wine at me? Do I need one?

Health headlines are forever championing the benefits of red wine, and now it looks as though you might be able to add your ears, or at least your hearing, to the list of its protective effects. Two studies presented at an academic meeting in London have found that antioxidants such as those found in a fruity Shiraz can help to stave off damage to the delicate hair cells in the inner ear. These hair cells turn sound waves into electrical signals that the brain can understand. But over a lifetime lifestyle factors and drugs produce harmful substances called free radicals which damage these cells, reducing their numbers and leading to hearing loss in old age. So researchers wondered whether antioxidants might have a hearing-preserving effect. Jochen Schacht, from the University of Michigan Medical School, gave patients receiving the antibiotic gentamicin, which is known to damage hearing, doses of the antioxidant salicylate alongside their antibiotics. At the end of the trial only 3% of patients given gentamicin and salicylate developed hearing loss, compared with 13% given the antibiotics accompanied by a placebo. In the second study, Matti Anniko, from the University of Uppsala in Sweden, found that antioxidants could reduce the severity of another ear disorder linked to hearing disruption: Ménière's disease. Schacht points out that although as yet there is no formal evidence that antioxidants like those found in red wine can prevent age-related hearing loss, studies on rats fed a strict diet intended to minimise free radical production showed considerably reduced hearing loss as they aged compared with rats fed the rodent equivalent of junk food. So there is every reason to think that boosting your antioxidant intake, including the resveratrol found in red wine, could help to keep you hearing well into old age.

Security
Laser technology

Are you saying that authenticity tags and holograms may be a waste of money?

Researchers at Imperial College, London, have shown that materials such as paper, plastic cards and product packaging have a surface structure that is as individually unique as a fingerprint. In fact, the chances of two surfaces having an identical surface 'barcode' of imperfections may be less than 1 in 1-followed-by-72-zeros! James Buchanan and his colleagues scanned the surfaces of materials with a laser and recorded the scatter pattern of light produced by each. Upon re-scanning a few days later after 'normal handling', their system was able to identify every single one without difficulty, even if pieces of paper had been screwed up or soaked in water and allowed to dry. They point out that, better still, no modification of the present product is required to implement their security measure!

Ecology
Electricity

Now, where in Europe would you be guaranteed to find a lot of wind?

UK energy supplier Scottish Power is about to erect the European Union's biggest on-shore wind farm, called Whitelee: 140 turbines will be erected on a 55-square-kilometre (21-square-mile) moorland and forest site south of Glasgow. It is due for completion in 2009, will cost £300 million and is expected to generate 322 Mw.

Diseases and disorders
Non-human biology

Surely it would be possible to get a 'good' bacterium to attack a 'bad' one?

Scientists at Nottingham University in England, together with their colleagues at the Max Planck Institute in Tübingen, Germany, are working on a potential living antibiotic – a predatory bacterium that hunts down and eats other bugs, but that does not harm human cells. Called *Bdellovibrio* the bacterial predator uses chemical sensors to home in on its prey. It locks on to the surface of other bacteria, including the gut-bug *E. coli*, using tiny bacterial grappling hooks called pili, and uses a cocktail of powerful enzymes to drill a hole in the cell wall of its prey. It then squeezes inside the target bacterium, which remains alive while this is going on, through the hole it has made. Once inside, it seals over the hole it made to get in and sets about digesting its prey from the inside out, growing as it does so. Once the supply of nutrients runs out, the now much larger predator splits up into between 15 and 60 smaller versions of itself which burst out from the dead husk of the bacterium, and all leave in search of fresh bacteria to eat. Microbiologist Liz Sockett and her team are now analysing the DNA blueprint of the *Bdellovibrio* bacterium in order to find out how to make some of the chemicals that it uses so successfully to attack other bacteria. More exciting than that, they are also planning to try to use the bacterium itself as a living antibiotic capable of hunting down and killing infections. This seems plausible because it doesn't trigger serious reactions in animals and it cannot infect mammalian cells. As soon as it ran out of bugs to eat, therefore, it would stop multiplying and could be removed from the body.

Genetics
Food and drink

Did *you* know how important yeasts are to life as we know it – I mean, to beer?

US researcher Kevin Verstrepen and his colleagues have described the mechanisms used by fungi and yeasts to stay one step ahead of our immune system. The team has found that like movie shape-shifters, the surfaces of yeast cells – which are the parts recognised by the immune system – change readily to avoid detection. They do this almost like an accordion by increasing or decreasing the length of repetitive pieces of DNA in the genes which control their surface appearance. As the genes become longer or shorter they can swap places with other nearby genes, altering the appearance of the cell and making it more difficult for the immune system to recognise it, explaining why fungal infections can be so difficult to treat. These inflating and deflating genes also hold the key to a cool clear beer, because some of them control a family of surface anchor molecules that lock yeasts together and also help them to glue themselves onto surfaces. The key to a crystal clear beer is therefore a yeast in which these genes are highly active so that they form clumps and settle out readily. Otherwise, you get a cloudy pint. Ugh!

Factoid:
'More tornadoes hit the UK each year than any other European country.'

TRUE
Yes, but that does not mean the UK gets very many. Dr Nikolai Dotzek from the Institute for Atmospheric Physics in Germany, estimates that 50 twisters hit the UK annually. Despite rumours to the contrary, the UK is *not* part of the USA.

Security
Genetics

Don't we need all the help we can get, to clear the existing minefields?

Scientists in Denmark have produced a genetically modified cress plant that can detect landmines in soil. Carsten Meier and his colleagues from Aresa Biodetection, the company they have set up to develop the GM strain of *Arabidopsis thaliana* or Thale cress, have genetically modified the plant to make it change colour from green to red when it grows near an unexploded mine. Nitrogen dioxide gas released by the breakdown of TNT, the explosive used in 99% of landmines, triggers the plant to produce anthocyanin, the naturally-occurring plant pigment that colours beetroot and makes autumn leaves turn red. The colour change takes about three weeks to develop, although the scientists don't yet know how sensitive the cress is at detecting all the landmines in an area, and whether the technology will work in all types of soil. There are also concerns that open fields full of lush cress could attract livestock into the mined areas. But with an estimated 110 million landmines claiming 2,000 victims per week across 70 countries worldwide, and the best de-mining personnel capable of clearing just 2 square metres (2½ square yards) of land a day, Meier and his team are confident that their genetically modified cress plant can make a significant contribution to the detection and clearance of landmines, particularly from agricultural land.

Diseases and disorders
Medicine

Is there any way of quickly identifying bacteria loose in hospital wards?

Working with doctors in Birmingham, scientists at the University of Warwick in England have developed an electronic 'nose' capable of sniffing out hospital superbug infections in a fraction of the time usually required for a traditional diagnosis. Surgeon David Morgan and engineer Ritaban Dutta's e-nose takes just 15 minutes to identify the smell-fingerprint of *Staphylococcus aureus*, a major cause of hospital infections. The machine, which is about the size of a pair of desktop PCs and costs about US $114,500 (£61,000), was trained to recognise the unique cocktail of volatile compounds produced by *Staph* bacteria using nasal swabs collected from people known to carry the bug. When it was then tested on clinical samples collected from hospital patients with a range of different infections, the e-nose successfully picked up 96% of the patients infected with *Staph*. Although it cannot yet discriminate between the problem-bug MRSA (which is the methicillin-resistant form of the same *Staph* bacterium) and its less harmful counterparts, the researchers suggest that it can be used to prioritise samples which might contain MRSA, so that they they can be diagnosed more quickly.

Human biology
The senses

'Baby, I am now going to read out the two times table. Baby, can you hear me in there?'

Researchers in America have discovered that the unborn baby can probably hear a lot more of what we say than we thought previously. Ken Gerhardt and Robert Abrams, from the University of Florida, implanted a tiny microphone into the inner ear of a lamb developing inside its mother, and then played 64 recorded sentences on a loudspeaker near to the mother sheep. For comparison they also placed microphones in the uterus (womb) and in the open air next to the sheep. They then asked 30 human adults to listen to the recordings from the various microphones and repeat what they heard. The volunteers understood all of the sentences recorded in the open air, about 70 per cent of the sentences recorded in the womb, and 30 per cent of the sentences recorded in the foetal sheep's inner ear. On the whole the researchers found that low-frequency sounds were heard better than high-frequency ones. Lead researcher Ken Gerhardt said that the intelligibility of sentences was 'actually much higher than we anticipated'. As for music, 'They're not going to hear the violins, but they will hear the drums,' said Gerhardt. This research is important because it has implications for babies born prematurely and placed in noisy baby units where there tend to be lots of high-pitched sounds which a baby of that developmental age would not normally be exposed to.

Food

Medicine

So now everyone can eat everything round the barbie?

Genetically modified (GM) prawns will soon be on the menu for people with seafood allergies. Scientists from New Orleans have altered a protein in prawns called tropomyosin which is responsible for most seafood allergies, making their GM prawns potentially allergen-free.

Electricity

You mean, someone has miniaturised a petrol-driven power-generator?

Scientists at Birmingham University in England have developed tiny engines only a few millimetres across that could soon replace standard batteries. Smaller than a fingernail the minature motors run on lighter fuel and produce 300 times more energy than a standard battery, which means that they can charge up laptops and mobile phones in a matter of seconds. The new motors are also much more energy-efficient than normal batteries. According to the project leader Dr Kyle Jiang, 'It takes 2,000 times more energy to manufacture a battery than the battery dispenses. Soon everyone will be able to recharge their mobiles instantly using a shot of cigarette-lighter fuel.' It's believed that the new motors could be on the market within six years. Their use could be extended to a wide range of applications including powering tiny spy cameras or minature robots, or micro-factories.

Food
The mind

Shall I compare thee to a summer's day?
Or perhaps to an ice cream sundae?

They say the way to a man's heart is through his stomach, but it looks as if it might be time for a re-think. That's because researchers at the Institute of Psychiatry at King's College, London, using fMRI brain scans, have found that when men and women are shown pictures of food, it is the women's brains that light up in anticipation, even if they aren't hungry. Rudolf Uher and his colleagues studied 18 male and female volunteers both when they were well fed and when they had fasted for 24 hours. During the trial the subjects were shown pictures of food, or even given food to eat, while researchers watched how their brains responded. In all cases a part of the brain called the occipitotemporal cortex lit up, but always more strongly in women than in men, irrespective of whether they had eaten or not. This part of the brain monitors how other brain regions, including those concerned with hunger or pleasure sensations, respond to food. So these findings show that the females in the study were engaging in more conscious thought and decision-making in response to the food stimuli presented by the researchers. But why? The researchers think that answer might lie in social pressure and be a learned response. Indeed, they are now looking at patients with eating disorders, 90% of whom are women. They have found that when anorexic or bulimic females are presented with images of food, they show far more activity in the occipitotemporal region of the brain than healthy women, reflecting their increased sensitivity to food. The team now plans to look at obese individuals to see how they compare.

Genetics

Doesn't that make the happy mother grateful for ova and ever?

US doctors have described the case of a woman who has become the world's first mother to give birth following an ovarian transplant. Stephanie Yarber developed ovarian problems at the age of 14 which rendered her infertile. Egg donation proved ineffective, so at the age of 24 Stephanie turned to her identical twin sister, who already had three children, for help. Her twin, Melanie, agreed to donate one of her ovaries, which was implanted onto Stephanie's own ovarian tissue last year. Shortly afterwards, she conceived normally, and in due course gave birth to a healthy baby girl. There were no problems with tissue incompatibility because the two women are identical twins, and thus genetically identical. But more importantly, as the medical team point out, this result shows that it is possible for a woman to have ovarian tissue removed and stored outside her body ('put on ice') – for instance, while she is undergoing chemotherapy for cancer, or just to delay childbirth – and the stored tissue can then successfully be re-implanted where it can restore full fertility.

Weather forecasting
Microwave technology

How can the fact that mobile phones are affected by bad weather be useful?

Researchers in Israel have found that mobile phone masts might be able to help weather forecasters monitor rainfall – but not in the way anybody might have expected. Hagit Messer and his colleagues at Tel Aviv University have shown in a study that because water absorbs the microwave signals used by mobile phones, masts have to compensate for rainy weather by upping their output power. Recording what output the masts are putting out therefore provides a continuous measurement of rainfall. In their trial their method turned out to be more accurate than conventional radar measurements, and nearly as good as the gold standard – a rain gauge. But although rain gauges are slightly more accurate, they are costly and cannot provide the same coverage or continuous measurement that the mobile technology can offer. In addition, it may also be possible to extend the approach to monitor atmospheric pollution including particulates, fog, sleet and hail. That would not necessarily add to the accuracy of national weather forecasts but could in time lead to sufficient quantities of data being gathered to add to information about local weather trends and directionality in a variety of weather circumstances.

Ecology

Does global warming mean that birds are having to make seasonal adjustments?

Migrating birds are certainly being hit hard by global warming because they are arriving home too late after winter. Christiaan Both, of the Netherlands Institute of Ecology, followed up nine populations of pied fly-catchers, which over-winter in Africa before returning to Europe in the spring to mate. But recent warmer temperatures in Europe have meant that the caterpillars that the birds rely on to feed to their young emerged much earlier than normal and had all but disappeared by the time the birds arrived and began to breed. As a result the populations of the birds in some areas where the effects were most marked declined by 90%.

Sport

Laser technology

Aren't you assuming that your first drive takes you within sight of the flag?

A US company, Laser Link Golf, has developed a handheld laser range-finding system which can accurately determine the distance to the flag. The shaver-sized device runs on a 9-volt battery. Pressing a trigger and pointing it at the pin starts the device emitting pulses of laser light. These are bounced back by a small five-sided reflector mounted on top of the flag. The time taken for the reflection to return gives the distance from the hole, accurate to within one or two metres/yards. So far the device is proving especially popular with caddies!

Astronomy

Somewhere out there, is something saying 'Somewhere out there, is something saying ...'?

Scientists at the Geneva Observatory in Switzerland have discovered three planets, similar in many ways to the Earth, orbiting a nearby star, HD69830, which is 41 light years away and just visible in the night sky. The newly-discovered Neptune-sized planets, which have been described by Christophe Lovis and his colleagues, mark the first time that scientists have been able to spot planets this small orbiting distant stars. The team used a system called the high-accuracy radial velocity planet searcher (HARPS) at the European Southern Observatory's telescope at La Silla, Chile, to study HD69830, which is about the same size as our own sun but twice its age. The planets themselves are too small to see directly, but HARPS enabled the researchers to spot a wobble in the star's path through space, which could only be produced by the gravitational effects of a clutch of orbiting planets. The three bodies range from 10 to 18 times the size of the Earth, are rocky and icy, and orbit their star in 9, 30 and 200 days respectively. Intriguingly, the planet orbiting in 200 days is at a distance from the star referred to as the 'habitable zone', where conditions are likely to permit the existence of liquid water. The discovery of HD69830 in any case marks the beginning of an era during which it is certain that the first Earth-like planets will be found orbiting distant stars.

Medicine

Is it true that skin grafts using foetal skin tissue may be better than ordinary skin grafts?

Doctors in Switzerland have been able to use tissue engineered from a foetus as an alternative to skin grafts in eight children with serious burns. Patrick Hohlfeld and his colleagues from the University Hospital of Lausanne used a small skin sample from a terminated 14-week pregnancy to produce a large amount of artificial skin which could be grafted onto injured skin in patients admitted to their hospital with burns. The foetal grafts resulted in rapid healing of the wound site without the need to harvest a skin graft from another part of the body. A genetic test on a healed area carried out in one patient showed that the patient's own skin had completely replaced the foetal tissue by the time the wound had closed. Foetal skin – the use of which is controversial in many countries and altogether banned in some – is well known for its ability to heal rapidly and without scarring, suggesting that it has the capacity to produce the right cocktail of growth factors to promote normal tissue regeneration, probably accounting for the success seen in the eight patients treated in this trial. It should perhaps be noted that those patients were themselves children, not adults.

Sound
Crime

Me? No, officer, I wasn't speeding –
I was just in the wrong gear, wasn't I?

Speed demon motorists watch out – the police may soon have a new weapon up their sleeves with which to trap you. And it works just by listening to the sound your car makes as it travels past a microphone. The novel trap technology, which is being developed by researchers at the University of Tennessee and Battelle Institute in Oak Ridge, relies on the Doppler effect – the way a sound alters in pitch as a moving object approaches and then passes the listener – to calculate the speed of passing vehicles. And because it relies only on a passive microphone, which eavesdrops silently on a car's engine note, motorists have no chance of being able to detect it and slam the brakes on to avoid a fine. To prove that the idea works, the development team recorded the noises made by a number of moving vehicles and then calculated their speeds based on the Doppler shift of the sounds made in each case. The system was right to within a few per cent in 32 out of 33 of these trials. It can even work out how large an engine is by listening to the sounds of the pistons, and whether a vehicle is overloaded by comparing the change in road speed relative to the change in engine load as the vehicle climbs an incline.

Medicine
Drugs

Hasn't it *always* been sensible to know how a patient will react to a drug?

Researchers in England have come up with a robust way to predict how different drugs might affect different people. Called pharmaco-metabonomics, it relies on little more than a splash of urine. Jeremy Nicholson and his team at Imperial College, London, had been looking for a way to realise the dream of pharmaco-genomics, which is essentially medicine tailor-made to an individual's genetic make-up. But the problem with trying to study genes is that there are so many variations and combinations in the population, and it is extremely difficult to predict how they all interact. Further-more, just focusing on the genes a person is carrying is not the whole story either, because it ignores the effect of environmental influences including what a person eats and drinks, and even what bacteria they are carrying in their intestines. A better approach, argues Nicholson, is to look at body fluids – like urine – because the composition of these is determined by interactions of all of a person's genes *and* the environment. In other words, the body produces its own 'chemical signature', which can in turn be used to predict how certain drugs will behave, or even to which illnesses a person might succumb. To test the idea the team at Imperial measured the urine of rats before and after a dose of para-cetamol. By using a computer model to compare the pre-dose and post-dose urine profiles, the researchers were able to predict what would happen to the rats when the drug was administered. This approach should help to make drug trials safer – currently a matter of considerable discussion in the UK – and improve the effectiveness of the drug cocktails that doctors dish out to their patients.

Sociology

Have *you* ever had to explain away an embarrassing tattoo?

The days of indelibly pledging your undying love for someone by tattooing his or her name across your forehead, only to regret it later, are finally over. Thankfully for those tempted to have 'Sharon forever' etched into their dermis, dermatologist Rox Anderson, from the Massachusetts General Hospital in Boston, has developed a way to produce erasable tattoos. He has found a way to encapsulate tattoo dyes within tiny polymer beads measuring between 1 and 3 thousandths of a millimetre across. When these dye capsules are scratched into the skin they are picked up by skin cells which then take on the colour of their encapsulated cargo, forming a tattoo. But if you decide subsequently that you don't like what you see, or if Sharon is superseded by Karen (or even Darren), a single blast with a laser can wipe the slate clean. It works because the laser breaks open the capsules, spilling the coloured contents that they contain, which is then absorbed and broken down. This is a marked improvement on existing tattoo technology which, in addition to using dyes that are also used in car paints and contain toxic chemicals such as heavy metals, can only be removed half of the time, and only then following fairly aggressive laser skin treatments.

Ecology
Chemistry

How can we economise as reserves of fossil fuels dwindle?

US researchers at Rutgers University in New Jersey have come up with a catalyst combination that might help to safeguard fuel supplies into the future. Alan Goldman and his colleagues have found a way to stitch together short hydrocarbon molecules, which come from coal, biomass, or refinery waste products, to make longer chains that are perfect for diesel fuel. To achieve this feat, which is known as alkane metathesis, the team have developed a pair of catalysts which work in tandem. The first knocks the hydrogens off one end of the short molecules, making them much more reactive, and the second then sticks the two pieces together to yield a longer-chain result. In some cases molecules of between 10 and 18 carbon atoms were produced, ideal for diesel. At the moment the catalysts are still under development and too inefficient to be used commercially, partly because they are too unstable and break down under the high temperatures (175°C/350°F) inside the reaction vessel. But with oil prices hitting the roof, supplies dwindling, and more cars than ever hitting the roads, a system that can turn plant waste into diesel – which this ultimately can – could rescue the petrochemical industry from an uncertain future.

Light
Physics
Safety

Who needs lights when the motorbike itself is all aglow?

Japanese manufacturer Yamaha has come up with a way to make motorcycles that are safer and easier for other road users to see – by developing a glow-in-the-dark film. The phosphorescent polymer soaks up ultraviolet rays from sunlight like an energy sponge. When the UV interacts with chemicals in the material it temporarily catapults electrons to a higher energy state. After darkness falls, the electrons slowly drop back down to their former unexcited state, releasing the energy in the form of a soft glow. Yamaha have come up with a vacuum process that can apply an even layer of the phosphorescent material over irregularly-shaped fairings, engine covers or cowlings. But above all Yamaha is hoping that the new range of 'glow-tor' bikes will make the roads a safer place for riders.

Safety
Laser technology

How can you keep birds consistently off airport runways?

An Israeli company, Dim Arizot Ltd, has come up with a novel way – by disorienting them with a laser. In the patent application the designers describe a disco mirror globe onto which several laser sources shine, firing light out in all directions. The device apparently dissuades birds from making a landing in the vicinity and does not cause long-term harm.

Medicine

Drugs

Quite a number of harmful bacteria are now drug-resistant, aren't they?

Researchers in the USA have uncovered a new antibiotic compound which is effective against drug-resistant bacteria including the notorious 'hospital superbug' MRSA. Jun Wang and Mike Soisson, from Merck Research Laboratories in New Jersey, have unveiled platensimycin, a small molecule naturally produced by the soil-dwelling bacterium *Streptomyces platensis*, which uses it to ward off the advances of other bacteria. Tests show that it is highly effective against what are called Gram-positive bacteria, including MRSA, and Streptococci, which cause skin infections, sore throats, earaches and pneumonia. The drug works by throwing a molecular spanner into the bacterial metabolic production line. It blocks the action of a series of enzymes called FabF/B and FabH, which make fatty acids that are critical for the bugs' survival, including those found in the cell wall. So far it has been tested on cultured bacteria and in mice with bacterial infections where it showed considerable promise and was very well tolerated. The researchers are now looking for a way to extend the range of platensimycin to include also Gram-negative bacteria, like *E. coli*, which are currently resistant, probably because they are able to pump the drug out of their cells before it can have an effect. Nevertheless, this novel agent adds a promising new weapon to our dwindling antibiotic arsenal, and the Merck researchers are planning to move it into human clinical trials as soon as possible.

Diseases and disorders
Solar technology

Might it ever be possible to restore vision with a retinal implant?

One day it might. Researcher Laxman Saggere, of the University of Illinois at Chicago, is endeavouring to develop a solar-powered retinal implant capable of squirting tiny amounts of nerve transmitter chemicals that can activate other cells in the retina, potentially restoring vision in some forms of blindness. The prototype device consists of two components: a flexible silicon actuator disc 1.5 millimetres (one-sixteenth of an inch) across and 15 microns thick, and an adjacent solar cell. When light hits the solar cell, it generates an electrical charge. This, in turn, passes into a piezo-electric material called PZT (lead zirconate titanate), causing it to change shape and bend the actuator disc. In the future a reservoir containing the neuro-transmitter will be placed beneath the actuator so that the change in shape triggered by light will cause a small amount of transmitter to be sprayed onto a target retinal cell. By shrinking the device, and creating an array of multiple actuator 'pixels', it should be possible to recreate a version of the visual world and trigger retinal ganglion cells to transmit the information to the brain.

Medicine

Drugs

The body's reaction to a heart attack can actually increase internal damage, can't it?

A UK research team has developed a drug that could make a significant dent in the damage done by heart attacks and strokes. Mark Pepys, of University College, London, and his colleagues have produced a substance called bis(phosphocholine)-hexane which blocks a chemical found in the bloodstream called C-reactive peptide (CRP). When cells are damaged, by whatever process, CRP locks onto them and then activates a cascade of blood proteins called complement. This has a powerful pro-inflammatory effect, the idea being to help the body to get rid of diseased tissue. But unfortunately the immune system tends to be over-zealous in its response, and healthy tissues near by are also destroyed. This is so-called bystander damage, and in the case of a heart attack, or stroke, it leads to the death of large areas of healthy heart or brain tissue adjacent to the area directly affected by the disease process. This in turn leads to increased disability on the part of the patient. But the new drug locks onto CRP and temporarily stops it from unleashing this devastating cascade, greatly reducing the scale of the damage. In tests on animals the team found that it was safe and effective in preventing the damage normally triggered by CRP in a heart attack. Furthermore, they suggest that it might also prove very useful in other inflammatory conditions such as rheumatoid arthritis and inflammatory bowel disease. The researchers are now planning to set up clinical trials as soon as possible to determine whether the drug is as effective in humans.

Thematic index

Ageing 13a, 169a, 191

Aircraft 111a

Animals/animal biology *see*
    Non-human biology

Art and art history
- fake sculpture 77

Astro-geology
- asteroid Itokawa 110
- comet Tempel 1 134
- comet Wild 2 119
- meteorites 144
- planet Mars 27b

Astronomy
- asteroid Apophis (MN4)
    173
- Deep Impact probe
    mission 134
- Hayabusa mission 110
- meteorites 144
- meteors 42b
- 'outcast' from the Galaxy
    179a
- planet Mars 27b
- planet Pluto, moons 105
- planet Saturn 198
- star HD69830 (with
    planets) 217
- Stardust probe mission 119
- stars, and distance/time 91

Biosphere 26

Buildings 13b

Business and litigation
- trademarks/names 14

Chemistry
- alkane metathesis 222
- petrified wood 170
- scratch-resistance 29

Colour 94

Communications
- ant to ant 185b
- boring conversation 10
- bottles that speak 40
- cellphone *see* mobile
    phone (*below*)
- chimp-speak 138
- interstellar 69a, 90b
- mobile phone charge-up
    122a
- mobile phone deception 64
- mobile phone masts and
    weather forecasting 215
- mobile phone ringtones
- pigeon TV monitoring 124
- pub table to bar 27a
- rope rescue 55b
- scratch-free screens 29
- text messaging 118a, 143
- TV ads 35b
- voicemail labelling 162
- WiFi 2

Computer technology
- chips with everything 145a

- emotion recognition software 53a
- going organic 145a, 164
- LCD high-resolution
  screens 186
- microcircuits, number of
  145a
- real-time 'holography' 116
- screens 12b
- speaking bottles 40
- to replicate robots 97

Culture
- erasable tattoo 221
- hunting online 133
- meteorite as prized
  possession 144
- movie blockbusters or
  duds 79
- Swedish poetry 69a
- wedding rings 129b

Dentistry 96

Dinosaurs 76

Diseases and disorders
- AIDS test 185a
- allergic conditions 140,
  151
- Alzheimer's 67, 107
- avian flu 121
- bacterial attack 193, 207,
  224
- blindness 95a, 225
- blocked arteries 197
- blood clots 197
- brain injury 25
- burns, serious 218

- cancer and cancer
  therapies 46, 136, 188,
  201
- cancer and metastasis 51
- cervical cancer 188
- congestive heart failure
  81a
- Crohn's disease (of the
  intestines) 166
- cup of coffee and a
  cigarette 93
- cystic fibrosis 54
- dementia 154
- depression 111b
- diabetes 137b
- diagnosis by spectral
  analysis 195
- dogs, comparative study of
  158b, 179b
- Ebola 58a
- effects of marijuana 49
- embolisms 197
- flu 111b
- food poisoning 11, 31
- growth hormone
  deficiency 132
- haemopihilia, and gene
  therapy 89
- heart attack 226
- heart damage 161, 226
- HIV 58a, 137a
- hospital bacteria 210, 224
- leukaemia treatment side
  effects 204
- magnetophagy 65b
- malaria, forecasting 36
- male infertility 204
- mental illness, signs of
  168

- mouth and throat cancer 136
- MRSA (hospital) superbug 224
- multiple sclerosis 5
- osteoporosis 83
- *Staphylococcus* infections 210
- stroke 135b, 226
- tooth decay 96
- viruses 100, 121, 137a
  see also Medicine

DNA profiling 147

Domestic events
- boy meets girl 61, 95b
- children swallowing things 65a
- cup of coffee and a cigarette 93
- drying clothes 150a
- farmyard smells 7
- fishing 127
- funerals 13b
- killing garden slugs 82
- light bulbs 117
- loneliness 111b
- power shortages and cuts 84
- preening in the mirror 50
- toast from a toaster 115
- washing clothes 6a, 33
- washing wineglasses 37b

Drink *see* Food

Drugs/Drug and solvent abuse
- bis(phosphocholine)-hexane 226
- cannabinoids for dieting 190
- cocaine in Colombia 200b
- cocaine in the Po 35a
- coca plants 200b
- marijuana 49
- pharmaco-metabonomics 220
- treatment for Alzheimer's 107

Ecology
- airborne pollution 124, 139, 153
- alkane metathesis 222
- ant infestation 126
- ants looking after 'their' tree 88
- bacteria alive after 30,000 years 163
- bird migration changes 216a
- cultured meats 203
- diesel engines 139
- eucalyptus/koalas 22
- farming practice 19b, 48b
- fossil fuel economies 222
- frog camouflage 112
- garlic as a pesticide 82
- global warming 47, 216a
- grass as air filter 153
- ivory trading ban 65a
- koalas/eucalyptus 22
- leaf colour in autumn 57
- petrol engines 37a
- plants with chemical defences 71, 183

- plants with guardian mites 48a
- pollinating fish 26
- reindeer 47
- sea wall 199
- sperm whales 66
- traffic exhaust pollution 139
- wave power electricity 159
- water usage, economic 150a
- wind farm 206b

Education
- in remote Africa 45

Electricity
- backup power system 104b
- from genetically modified viruses 175a
- measures to save 84, 117
- medical use of 130
- miniature petrol-driven generator 212b
- mirrors and 108
- multi-charging pad 176
- portable charger 122a
- radioactivity and 122b
- recharging mat 176
- to provide grip 118b
- wave power 159
- wind farm 206b

Electronics
- computer screens 12b
- disk capacity 17
- scratch-free screens 29

Evolution 32, 87, 92, 120, 202

Fabric technology 125b, 180

Food/Food and drink
- alcoholic beverage 171
- badly cooked poultry 11
- beer 208
- beer mats 27a
- bottled water 69b
- chocolate that's good for you 74
- churchgoers and 106
- contaminated meat 55a
- diet and suggestibility 41
- diet drugs 190
- drink flavours 16
- edible menu 167
- fats 99, 187
- food poisoning diagnosis 31
- meat sheets 203
- nut-sorting 18
- olive oil 169b
- popcorn 24a
- prawns, genetically modified 212a
- processed meats 203
- red wine 63, 205
- tea 90a
- temptation with 123
- toast 115
- turmeric, properties of 67
- water 69b
- way to a (wo)man's heart 213
- yeasts 208

Forensic science 6b, 20, 147, 155a

Games and pastimes
- aggression in 56
- football 1

Genetics
- cloning 8, 78
- computer technology and 164
- Darwinian evolution 32, 87
- dog genome 158b
- dyslexia and 158a
- gene names 14
- genes for individuality 165b
- genes for liking fatty foods 187
- genes for making silk 125b
- genes in yeasts 208
- genes switching on or off 98a
- gene therapy for blindness 95a
- gene therapy for deafness 177
- gene therapy for haemo-philia 89
- gene therapy for mouth/throat cancer 136
- genetically modified bacteria 189a
- genetically modified cow 132
- genetically modified cress plant 209
- genetically modified prawns 212a
- mapping of territory 20
- mosquito control 73
- olfactory insect genes 141
- ovarian transplant leading to childbirth 214

Geology
- iron-60 deposits 92
- magnetic north/south 80
- quicksand 60
- terrestrial 4
  see also Astro-geology

Gyroscopes 75b

Heredity
- children and beauty 114a
- genes for individuality 165a
- mother and child 21

Histology
- bacterial attack mecha-nisms 146, 193
- cells switching on or off 98a
- cloning of animals 78a
- insect pheromone receptors 181
- mother and child 21
- robotics and 142
- skin cells ageing 169a
- sperm count in men 131
- stem cell research 102, 161, 179b, 189b, 194a
- Venus flytrap mechanism 174

Holography 116

Human biology
- addiction to caffeine/ nicotine 93
- age, activity and cognitive function 191
- age and balance 13a
- age and odour 113b
- attractiveness of children 114a
- bad breath 109
- bipedal development 92
- body odour 196
- bone accretion 129b
- bones thinning with age 83
- boy meets girl 61, 95b
- brain 25
- brain centre for sarcasm 85a
- brain size and intelligence 72
- brain waves and ageing 154
- brain waves during sleep 81b
- breathing 120
- breathing out chemicals 86
- cells, switching on or off 98a
- cholesterol 74
- collecting and hoarding 62
- digestion 42a
- dirt and deterring mosquitoes 196
- dirt and the need to wash 33
- emotion recognition 53a
- exhaling explosives 86
- facial expressions, recognition of 78b
- fatty food and blood vessels 99
- finger length 56
- fingerprints 6b
- foetal tissue for skin grafts 218
- genes for individuality 165b
- halitosis 109
- hearing in the unborn 211
- hoarding 62
- insulin and diabetes 137b
- intestinal flora 151
- keenness of olfactory sense 34
- kung fu ability 15
- laughter 68, 104a
- longevity and churchgoing 106
- meat-eating 48b
- microwaves, contact with 103b
- muscles and weight training 75b
- muscles in space 12a
- nerve activity in the stomach 155a
- obesity and appetite 114b
- obesity and sleep 52
- passive smoking and 150b
- puberty 78b
- skin cells ageing 169a
- sleep 3a, 24b, 52
- sperm count in men 131
- stem cells, non-embryonic 102
- stress and music 44

- stun-guns and 149
- susceptibility to infection
  111b, 121
- teeth and tooth decay 96
- veins and intravenous
  treatment 128
- visions of the future 50
- women's response to food
  213

Human statistics
- suicide 19a

Hydrography
- polar regions 23

Information technology
- disk capacity 17

Instinctual behaviour 165a,
  213

Laser technology 109, 149,
  197, 201, 204, 216b, 223b

Life-support systems
- beer mats 27a
- cup of coffee and a
  cigarette 93
- own 'special tree' 88
- Swedish poetry 69a
- toast 115

Light
- LED technology 117, 128,
  145b
- phosphorescence 223a
- refraction in glass 37b

- scatter pattern
  individuality 206a
- sound-sensitive lighting
  145b
- transforming plastics 135a

Marine ecology
- polar regions 23

Medicine
- AIDS test 185a
- anti-allergic measures
  212a
- antibacterial treatments
  146, 207, 210, 224
- antioxidants 63, 205
- bis(phosphocholine)-
  hexane 226
- brain injury 25
- cancer, knowledge of 51
- cancer therapies 46, 136,
  188, 201
- cervical cancer, vaccine
  for 188
- chemotherapy, effects of
  204
- cystic fibrosis 54
- dangers of caffeine and
  nicotine 93
- dangers of fatty foods 99,
  187
- dementia, treatment for
  154
- drugs for dieting/slimming
  190
- electrical activity, use of
  130
- electrogastrogram 155a
- food poisoning 31, 90a

- heart failure, congestive 81a
- hip replacement 175b
- HIV 58a, 137a
- hospital/care 2, 210
- human growth hormone 132
- immune system 42a, 151, 166
- immune system therapies 5, 140
- injections, simultaneous 200a
- intestinal flora 151
- intestinal worms as treatment 140, 166
- intravenous 39, 128
- living antibiotics 207
- lung function 54
- micro-robot surgery 157
- obesity 114b
- olive oil 169b
- ovarian transplant 214
- pacemaker 125a
- pharmaco-metabonomics 220
- prosthetics 135b
- red wine 63, 205
- retinal implant 225
- scanners for diagnosis 100
- skin grafts 218
- spectral analysis for diagnosis 195
- stem cell therapy on the heart 161, 179b, 194a
- surgery 135a, 157
- suspended animation, and hibernation 148
- tea 90a
- ultrasound advances 178
- worm treatment 140, 166
- wound dressings 182
  see also Diseases and disorders

Microwave technology 103b, 215

Military technology
- robot spy-planes 111a

Mind, the
- brain and brain power 72
- colours, and associations 94
- compulsion to hoard 62
- effect of alcohol 171
- effect of laughter 68, 104a
- memory 98a
- persistence of music 59
- planning ahead 202
- reaction to images of food 213
- sarcasm, as a brain function 85a
- suggestibility 41
- temptation with food 123, 213
- TV ad persuasiveness 35b

Non-human biology
- ants and fellow ants 185b
- ants and fungi 126
- ants and other ants 172
- ants and 'their' tree 88
- Australian cuttlefish, cross-dressing 194b
- birds and moths 192

- black bears and hibernation 83
- bonobos and foresight 202
- canary song 165a
- caterpillars under attack 183
- chimpanzees, scratching backs 184
- chimpanzees, 'talking' 138
- chipmunks and hibernation 148
- cloning 78a
- cuckoo 160
- dinosaurs, male and female 76
- dogs and wagging tails 85b
- dolphins in Australia 98b
- frog, ultrasound croaking of 156
- frogs and frog camouflage 112
- geckos and sticky feet 118b
- giant cuttlefish, cross-dressing 194b
- giant tortoise 'Mzee' 58b
- gorilla and pacemaker 125a
- hibernation 83, 148
- hippo 'Owen' 58b
- horses and handedness 152
- hummingbirds' memory 43
- insect pheromones 181
- insects' sense of smell 141
- ivory 65a
- koalas 22
- mammoths 65a
- mosquitoes 73, 196
- moths and birds 192
- orang-utans and foresight 202
- poison arrow frogs 112
- snails, travelling 32
- stem cell therapy for racehorses 189b
- village weaverbird and cuckoo 160
- whales with the bends 66

Palaeo-botany 170

Palaeontology 4, 38, 47, 65a, 76, 92, 120, 163

Petrol engines 37a

Photography 30a

Physics
- bacterial camera 189a
- breathalyser 86
- contrast for camouflage 192
- curve ball 1
- electrochromic textiles 180
- fluorescence 101, 204
- holograms 206a
- kung fu 15
- LCD technology 186
- LED technology 117
- magnetic north/south 80
- phosphorescence 223a
- porous sea wall 199
- toast with radioactivity 115

Plant biology
- anthocyanin (pigment) 209
- anti-caterpillar chemical defence 183
- carnivorous mite guardians 48a
- chemical communications 71
- fluorescent glow 101
- leaf colour in autumn 57
- Venus flytrap 174

Pollution control *see* Ecology

Pregnancy and maternity 8

Prosthetics 135b

Radioactivity 115, 122b

Robots/robotics
- guide 'dogs' 103a
- heart muscle cells and 142
- micro-robotic surgeons 157
- self-replicating 97

Safety/Security
- authenticity tags/ holograms 206a
- cycle lighting 30b
- minefield clearance 209
- motorcycle, phosphorescent 223a
- runway clearance of birds 223b

Senses, the
- bad breath 109
- balance 13a
- blindness 95a, 103a
- colour perception 94
- hearing 28, 177, 205
- hearing in the unborn 211
- mental equilibrium 19a
- music and 44, 59
- smell 7, 34, 109, 113b, 168, 196
- taste 16, 167
- taste for fatty foods 187
- vision 192, 225
- weariness 24b

Sleep 3a, 24b, 52, 81b

Sociology
- back-scratching 184
- boredom 10
- churchgoing 106
- colour, and associations 94
- dyslexia 158a
- learning in class 45
- live 'books' 3b
- loneliness 111b
- passive smoking 150b
- tattoos, erasable 221
- wedding rings 129b
- woman and man 61

Solar cell (photovoltaic) technology
- flexible solar panels 70
- handbag 155b
- mirror array 108
- retinal implant possibilities 225

- wearable charger 122a

Sound/Sound technology
- cochlear hearing-aid 28
- Doppler-shift speed trap
    219
- frog in ultrasound 156
- nut-sorting 18

Space
- agravitation 12a

Sport
- fishing 127
- golf, laser-assisted 216b
- hunting online 133
- team colours 94

Surgery 135a, 157, 175b

Ultrasound technology
- for medical purposes 39,
    178

Vehicles
- bicycles 30b
- car paint 53b
- car theft 75a
- motorbikes 223a
- portable zebra crossing
    113a

Weather
- forecasting 215
- long-range forecasting 36

X-ray technology/scanning
    9, 77

General index

Acers (maples) 57
acetophenone 29
acetylcholine neuro-
    transmitter 107
adaptation (odour
    habituation) 7
advanced denial
    system (ADS) 103b
aerolysin, bacterial toxin
    193
age and ageing 13a, 113b,
    169a, 191, 205
AIDS testing, instant 185a
aircraft and jumpy
    passengers 88f
air pressure at height 26f
alarm clock 3a, 81b
alcohol, effects of 171
alcohol, in antifreeze 130f
alkane metathesis 222
allergic conditions 140,
    151, 212a
Alzheimer's disease, effects
    of 67, 107
amyloid plaques, in
    Alzheimer's 107
ancient writings, recovered
    9
angiotensin hormones 63
animals of war 18f
Antarctic Ocean 23
antennae, insects' 172, 181
anthocyanin(s) 57, 209
anthrax detection 31, 195
antibiotic, living 207

antibiotic resistance 146,
    224
antibiotics 163f, 182, 205
anti-cancer therapies 51,
    201
antifreeze and antifreeze
    poisoning 130f
antioxidants 63, 67, 74, 205
anti-wrinkle creams 169a
ants 19b, 88, 116f, 126,
    172, 185b
appearance, predicting
    one's 50
Archimedes palimpsest 9
arsenic, effects of 127f
arterial disease and
    prevention 63, 68, 93,
    135a, 197
Arctic Ocean 23
artificial gravity 12a
artificial skin 218
artificial throat 16
asteroid Apophis (MN4)
    173
asteroid Itokawa 110
asthma 140, 151
astronaut(s) 12a
atmospheric temperature
    71f
Australia 4, 11, 13b, 22,
    87, 98b, 110, 194b
auditory association area
    (brain) 59
authenticity tags, needless
    206a
autism 10
autoimmune diseases 21
avian flu, spread of 121

baby 8, 21, 139f
baby, unborn 211
background noise elimination 64
back-scratching as sign of cognitive capacity 184
bacteria, ancient but 'alive' 163
bacteria, 'bad' 11, 55a, 69b, 109, 146, 195, 207, 210, 224
bacteria, 'good' 11, 42a, 146, 151, 166, 207
bacteria, light-sensitive 189a
bacterial camera 189a
bacterial toxin(s) 146, 193
bad breath (halitosis) 109
bad eating habits 41
balance, sense of 13a
ball (= football) 1
battery, from a genetically modified virus 175a
Battery Energy Storage System (BESS) 104b
Bdellovibrio bacteria 207
beards, and health 153f
beauty and the beast 61
bed 3a
bedsores, healing of 130
beef 55a
beer, clear 208
beer, pleasantly warm 27a
beer mat, electronic 27a
Beijing, air conditions 153
bends, the (caisson disease) 66
beta-amyloid protein 67

betanin fluorescence nullifying agent 101
betaxanthin pigment 101
Big Bang, the 91
birds, ancestry of 38, 76
birds, migratory 32, 216a
birds' eggs, and cuckoos' 160
birds on airport runways 223b
black bears and hibernation 83
black hole at centre of the Galaxy 179a
bleeding in the brain 25
BLILO digital camera 30a
blindness, possible therapy for 95a, 225
blog(s) 90b, 124
blood-alcohol levels 171
blood-clotting Factor IX 89
bloodflow, through the brain 49
blood infusion 39
blood vessels, narrowing/narrowed 49, 63, 68, 93, 99, 197
blue, significance of the colour 94
Blu-ray data storage 29
body odour as insect repellent 196
bone, weight of 149f
bone-grown wedding rings 128b
bone marrow cells 51
bone-thinning diseases 83
bonobos, foresighted 202

book(s) 3b
boredom detector 10
bottle that talks 40
box-office hit prediction
    79
brain, size of human 72
brain, weight of human
    172f
brain centre for music 59
brain centre for sarcasm
    85a
brain changes at puberty
    78b
brain-derived neurotrophic
    factor (BDNF) 160f
brain function, deteriorating
    154, 191
brain injuries/damage 25,
    85a, 99
brain waves and dementia
    154
brain waves during sleep
    81b
breathalyser 86
breathing/respiration 121
British military animals 18f
bullsh*t 7
burglars, and their DNA
    147

caffeine, effects of 93
caisson disease 66
calcium, in bones 83
calcium, in shells 76
calcium carbonate 9f
camels' humps 168f
camera 30a
camera, comprising bacteria
    189a

camouflage, animal 112,
    192
camouflaging textiles 180
Campylobacter 11
canaries, teaching to sing
    165a
cancer and cancer cells 46,
    51, 67, 80, 136, 177,
    188, 201, 204
cannabinoids as diet drugs
    190
car, starting a cold 37a
car batteries 33f
carbon dioxide, atmospheric
    48b, 84
cardiac fibrosis 63
cardiac pacemaker, for a
    gorilla 125a
cardiac resynchronisation
    therapy (CRT) 125a
care institution 2
car keys 75a
Carnobacterium
    pleistocenium 163
carotenoids, in tree leaves
    57
car paintwork 53b
carpenter ants 126
car theft 75a
Cassini probe, to Saturn
    198
catalytic converter, petrified
    wood as 170
catechin, poisonous
    substance 57
caterpillars and plant
    defences 183
CDs 17
Cdx2 (gene) 8

cellphone *see* mobile phone

cells, body 8, 21

central nervous system *see* nerves

centrifuge 12a

cerebral cortex, human 72

cervical cancer, vaccine against 188

chalk 9f

chameleon suit 180

charger, portable/wearable 122a

charging pad/mat 176

chef, innovative 167

chemical signals 71

chemotherapy, effects of 204

chicken (meat) 11, 55a

chickens 11

children, attractive and ugly 114a

children, full of bones 197f

children's abilities, aged five 191f

chimpanzees, and back-scratching 184

chimpanzees, and 'talking' 138

chocolate, cholesterol-reducing 74

chocolates, as tempting bait 123

cholesterol, 'bad' (LDL) 74

cholesterol, 'good' (HDL) 74, 190

chromosome(s) 139f, 158a

chromosomes, X and Y 139f

churchgoers and longevity 106

churchgoing and diet 106

cinnamon as sleep inhibitor 24b

ciprofloxacin, antibiotic 182

cliffs 9f

climate change 23

climate prediction 36

'Clocky' 3a

clones and cloning 8, 78a

cocaine 35a, 200b

coca plants 200b

cochlear implants 28

cocolithophores 9f

coffee with a cigarette 93

cola drinks 19b

cold, the common 163f

collagen 63, 130

collecting, fixation for 62

Colombia and cocaine trade 200b

colour-change, of leaves 57

colour-changing textiles 180

colours, effect of 94

colours that run 6a

comet 42b, 119, 134

common cold, the 163f

complement, blood proteins 226

computer, hand-held 10

computer foot-pedals 203f

computerised systems 53a, 116

computer predictions 50

computer screen 12b

computer technology, and organic elements 145a, 164

concrete-block-smashing 15

continental drift, inexorable 91f

contrasting colours as camouflage 192

conversation 10

corn (maize), defence against insects 183

corn for popcorn 24a

cosmic rays, and the Earth 92

country music 19a

C-reactive peptide (CRP) 226

crematorium 13b

Cretaceous Period 9f

Crohn's disease, treatment of 166

crop spraying 19b

cross-adaptation 7

cross-dressing cuttlefish 194b

crowd control 103b, 149

Cryptosporidium bacteria 195

CT scan 25

cuckoos and other birds' eggs 160

curve(d) ball 1

cuticular hydrocarbons exuded by ants 172

cuttlefish, cross-dressing 194b

cycling safety 30b

cystic fibrosis 54

cytoskeleton of skin cells 169a

Darwin, Charles 32, 87, 114a, 174

data storage 17

deaf(ness) 28, 177, 205

decompression sickness 66

Deep Impact comet probe 134

dementia, prediction of 154

dental fillings, trouble-free 96

depression, in men 56

detergent, surfactant 150a

'Devil's gardens' in Amazonia 88

diabetes 21, 137b, 190

diagnosis, new methods 136

diesel engine 120f, 139

diesel fuel 222

dietary habits 41

diet drugs, cannabinoids as 190

digestion, human body 42a

digital camera 30a

digital disk 17

dinosaur(s) 38, 76

dirt-resistant fabric 33

diseases, endemic 36

disk, electronic information 17

divers and the bends 66

DNA profiles lifted from food 147

dog, genome of 158b

dogs and wagging tails 85b

dolphins wearing nose-sponges 98b
Doppler-shift-based speedtrap 219
dragline silk, genes for 125b
dragonflies 26
Dresser Formation, the 4
drink flavours 16
drinking glasses 2
driving and falling asleep 24b
drug, personal reactions to 220
drug capsules, intradermal 200a
drying clothes in a washtub 150a
Duroia hirsuta trees 88
DVDs 17, 79
dye(s) 6a
dynamos for bicycle lights 30b
dyslexia, as genetic disorder 158a

$E = mc^2$ 40f
ears, evolution of 120
Earth's earliest inhabitants 4
'ear worms' 59
eating disorders 213
eating unhealthily 41
Ebola (disease) 58a
E. coli bacteria 31, 195, 207
education in remote Africa 45
egg (ovum) 8

Eiffel Tower, the 22f
elderly, the 13a, 191
electrical activity in the body 130
electric bandage 130
electricity, measures to save 84
electricity generation 70, 104b, 108, 122b, 159, 206b, 212b
'electrochromic' textiles 180
electroencephalogram (EEG) 154
electrogastrogram (EGG) 155a
elephants and ivory 20
elephant seals 23
embryo 8, 98a
emotion-recognition software 53a
Emotive Alert voicemail labelling 162
endangered species 22, 47
endothelium of blood vessels 68
endorphins 114b
epidermal growth factor receptor (EGFR) 46
epidural haematomas 25
equator, atmosphere 71f
erasable tattoos 221
Escherichia see *E.coli*
estrogen *see* oestrogen
eucalyptus trees 22
European Southern Observatory 217
evolution, human 92

exercise, retaining
  brainpower 191
explosives 6b, 86
eye, human 187f
eyesight, restoration of 225

facial expressions 10, 78b
fall(s) 13a, 25
falling asleep 24b
farmyard smells 7
fatigue, effects of 24b
fatty foods, and heredity
  187
fatty food, effects of 99
fertility, female 214
fertility, male 204
fetus *see* foetus
finger length, and
  aggression 56
fingernail growth rate 91f
fingerprinting 6b
fish and eggs 45f
fish and pollination 26
fishing line breaking point
  127
flavonoids, antioxidants 74
flavours in drink 16
flora, intestinal *see*
  intestinal flora
flu, susceptibility to 111b
fluorescence-activated cell-
  sorting (FACS) 204
fluorescent flowers 101
fluorine 29
foetal skin tissue 218
foetus 8, 21, 211
food, and women's reaction
  213
food poisoning 11, 31, 90a

foot-pedals for computer
  operation 203f
fossil fuel, economies in
  222
fossils, dinosaur 76
fossils, prehistoric fish 120
free radicals 205
frog camouflage 112
frog croaking in ultrasound
  156
fruit bats, and viruses 58a
fruit flies 141
fuel, motor 37a, 222
fungal infection/infestation
  69b, 208
fungal pesticide 126

GABA, inhibitory neuro-
  transmitter 171
game(s) 1, 94
gamma-ray burst mapping
  91
garlic, as pesticide 82
gastrointestinal magnets
  65b
geckos and grippy toes
  118b
gene(s) 8, 73, 98a, 125b,
  136, 141, 158a, 165b,
  177, 187, 208
gene monitoring 136
gene names 14
generators, power/
  electricity 84, 212b
genes, 'jumping' 165b
gene therapy and blindness
  95a
gene therapy and deafness
  177

gene therapy and haemophilia 89
genetically modified bacteria 132
genetically modified cow 132
genetically modified cress plant 209
genetically modified prawns 212a
genetically modified virus 89, 175a
genetic map of ivory DNA 20
genetic sequence(s) 32, 158b
genome, dog's 158b
genome, human 165b
gentamicin, antibiotic 205
giant Australian cuttlefish 194b
giant squid, injured 66
giant tortoise, 'Mzee' 58b
gills turning into ears 120
girls and boys, and presuppositions 95b
glaciation on Mars 27b
glass, defects in 37b
global warming 47, 216a
'glow-tor' motorbikes 223a
glow-worms and the war effort 18f
glycol, effects in the body of 130f
gold and gold salts 46
golf, laser range-finder for 216b
gorilla 'Babec' 125a

grapefruit smell and women of uncertain age 113b
grass planted for air filtration 153
greenhouse gases 4, 48b
grey matter 59, 72
growth factor injections 179b
growth factors and tissue regeneration 218
Guanlong wucaii 38
gyroscopic weight training 75b

H5N1 strain of avian flu 121
halitosis (bad breath) 109
hand(s) 15
handbag, solar-powered 155b
Hayabusa asteroid mission 110
HD69830, star 217
head injuries 25
healing of skin wounds 218
hearing, sense of 205
hearing, within the womb 211
hearing-aids 28
heart, as a pump 182f
heart attack 161, 226
heart disease/damage 63, 67, 74, 81a, 93, 161, 169b, 179b, 194a
heart enlargement 81a
heart muscle cells, in a robot 142
heart rate, monitoring 44

Heartsbreath breathalyser
    86
hibernation 83, 148
hibernation-specific protein
    (HP) 148
high-accuracy radial
    velocity planet searcher
    (HARPS) 217
hippo, 'Owen' 58b
hip replacement surgery
    175b
HIV diagnosis 185a
HIV patient(s) 69b
HIV spread 137a
hoarding, compulsion for
    62
holograms, needless 206a
Hong Kong 104a
hormone implant 22
horses, left- or right-
    'handed' 152
horses, treatment for
    189b
hospital environment 2
Hubble Space Telescope
    105
human growth hormone, in
    milk 132
human papilloma virus
    (HPV) 188
hummingbirds 43
humour, as treatment 68
hunting online 133
hydrochloric acid 33f
hydroxyapatite paste 96
hyrax 61f

ibuprofen, and olive oil
    169b

ice, in a freezer 147f
ice, on a comet 134
ice cream, bad experience
    with 41
Ig Nobel Prize 19a
immune system, human 5,
    42a, 89, 137b, 151, 188,
    208, 226
immunosuppressants,
    natural/organic 140, 166
implants see surgical
    implants
index finger 56
India 19b, 67
infection, susceptibility to
    111b
infertility, male 204
infrared light technology
    55a, 70
injections, simultaneous
    200a
inner ear damage/injury
    177, 205
insect pests 19b, 141
insect sense of smell 141,
    181
insulin formulation 137b
intelligence, human 72,
    101f
Internet 13b, 20, 90b
intestinal flora 11, 151
intestinal walls 65b
intestinal worms, as
    treatment 140, 166
intoxication, alcoholic 171
intravenous therapy 39,
    178
in-vitro fertilisation 102
IQs 72, 101f

iron atoms 9
iron deposits 92
ivory trading 20, 65a

'jumping' genes 165b
jumping on aircraft 88f

kerb-crawling, dangers of
    139
kettle 40f
kinetic energy 15
Kinkajou projector, the 45
kissing, tilting the head
    while 64f
koalas 22
kung fu 15

landmine detection, organic
    209
laptops and lap temperature
    131
laser stun-guns 149
laser technology and use
    46, 109, 149, 204, 206a,
    221
laughter as the best
    medicine 68, 104a
LCD screens 12b, 186
learning 45
LEDs 2, 30b, 45, 117, 128,
    145b
lemon shark, Caribbean 45f
leptin and ghrelin,
    hormones 52
leukaemia, chemotherapy
    for 204
library 3b
lie detection 155a

light, interference pattern in
    37b, 206a
light bulbs 117, 145b
lighting, sound-sensitive
    145b
line (rope, cord) 55b
Listeria bacteria 90a
lithium battery, improved
    version of 175a
'lovers' cups' 2
lung function 54, 121

magnetic field of the Earth
    80
magnetic north, polarity 80
magnetism and metals 83f
magnet-swallowing 65b
Magnus force 1
maize, resistance to insect
    attack by 183
malaria 36, 181, 195
mammals 61f
mammoth ivory 65a
Manchester's reds and blues
    94
manure 7
marijuana, effects of 49
Mars (planet) 27b, 163
Mars Express probe 27b,
    163
Mars rover Spirit 42b
meat, contaminated 55a
meat, cultured processed
    203
meat, vegetarian-friendly
    203
Mediterranean diet, benefits
    of 169b
memorial to animals 18f

memory 35b, 43, 98a, 160f
Ménière's disease 205
mental illness, predisposition toward 168
menu, edible 167
metastasis, cancer 51
meteorites, as collectables 144
meteor showers 42b
methane 4
methanol poisoning 130f
methyl jasminate 71
metrosexual man 61
mice, super-intelligent 97b
microcircuits with organic elements 145a, 164
microfilm 45
micro-gravity 12a
microrobot surgeons 157
microwave crowd control 103b
midnight feasts, reprehensible 52
migratory birds 32, 216a
mineral water(s) 69b
mirrors, and electricity generation 108
mites, carnivorous plant guardians 48a
mobile phone, background noise 64
mobile phone accessory 138f
mobile phone 'life-jacket' 138f
mobile phone masts, and the weather 215
mobile phone ring tones 129a

Mona Lisa, the 53a
moons of Pluto 105
mosquitoes, and blood 73, 83f
mosquitoes, and body odour 196
mosquitoes, and odour-detecting genes 141
motorbike that glows in the dark 223a
mountain-top, conditions at 26f
mouse trails 97b
mouth cancer 136
movie popularity prediction 79
MRSA infection 210, 224
mucus 54
Multiple Optical Data Storage (MODS) 17
multiple sclerosis 5
muscle 12a
muscle tone 12a
music, and stress 44
music, and unforgettability 59
music appreciation 28
myelin 5
myocardial infarct *see* heart attack
Mzee and Owen 58b

naked mole-rat 61f
NASA 42b
near-Earth objects (NEOs) 173
near-infrared technology 25, 46, 128, 201
nectar, of flowers 43

neon 106f
nerve fibres/nerve endings 5, 13a, 181
nerves, nervous system 13a, 24b, 130, 155a
neurological disease 5
Nicaragua 87
nicotine 71, 150b
nicotine addiction 150b
night-blooming flowers 101
nitric oxide, as relaxant 68
North Pole, atmosphere 71f
nostrils 34
nuts 18

obesity 52, 114b
obsessive compulsive disorder 62
occipitotemporal cortex, in women 213
oceans 23
odour 7, 33, 34, 113b, 141
oenology 40
oestrogen hormones 76
oleocanthal, anti-inflammatory 169b
olfactory system, human 34
oligonucleotides and electronics 164
olive oil, great benefits of 169b
olivine 119
orang-utans, foresighted 202
osteoporosis 83
ovarian transplant 214
overweight, drugs to be less 114b

Owen and Mzee 58b
owl, head rotatability of 178f
oxygen content of air 26f
ozone layer 80

pacemaker, cardiac 125a
pacemaker cells in a microrobot 142
Pampa Mansa, the Jersey cow 132
pancreas, and insulin production 137b
Panderichthys prehistoric fish 120
particle accelerator 9
peppermint as sleep inhibitor 24b
Perspecta three-dimensional 'screen' 116
petrified wood, synthetic 170
petrol engines 120f, 212b
pharmaco-metabonomics 220
phenylene vinylene 127
pheromones, insects' 181
phosphorescent polymer 223a
photos, taking 30a
physics 15
pied flycatchers, European 216a
piezo-electricity 28, 31, 142, 225
pigeons, and pollution monitoring 124
pistachio nuts 18
placebo 5

placenta 8, 21
plan ahead, ability to 202
planets of another star 217
planets of the solar system 42b, 198
plant defence mechanisms 183
plastics deformation and transformation 135a
platensimycin 224
Pluto, new moons of 105
pneumocytes in the lungs 121
Po, River 35a
poetry in Swedish 69a
poison arrow frogs and imitators 112
Pokemon (game) 14
pollination of flowers 26, 101
pollution, airborne 124, 153, 215
pollution at street level 139
polyglycidyl methacrylate 33
polymeric amines 6a
polyurethane 199
polyvinylidene fluoride 28
popcorn 24a
poultry (meat) 11
powerstations, electricity 84
prawns, non-allergenic 212a
prefrontal cortex of the brain 62, 72, 85a
prejudices 3b
pressure sensor 27a

pressure sores, healing of 130
probiotic bacteria 11
profoundly deaf 28
protective mechanisms of plants 48a
puberty, effects of 78b, 165a
pulsed energy projectile (PEP) 149
puppy fat, disadvantages of 128
PZT (lead zirconate titanate) 31, 225

'quantum dot' nanoparticles 117
quartz 4
quicksand 60

radiation exposure/detection 86
radioactivity in a toaster 115
railway track listening 15f
rain forecasting 215
range-finder, laser-operated 216b
recharger, electrical 176
red, significance of the colour 94
'red wall' limit for microchips 164
red wine, enormous benefits of 63, 205
reindeer and climate reliance 47
resveratrol, antioxidant 63, 205

retinal implant, to restore vision 225
retinitis pigmentosa 95a
rheumatoid arthritis, possible therapy for 226
rhythms, effect of 44
rimonabant (Acomplia), diet drug 190
ring finger 56
ring tones, unexpected 129a
river water 35a
road crossing 113a
robot, self-assembling 142
robot, self-replicating 97a
robot, with organic elements 142
robot arm for stroke patients 135b
robot 'guide dogs' 103a
robot spy-planes 111a
rope, for rescuing 55b
runways, clearing birds from 223b
RUPERT the prosthetic arm 135b

sagebrush, and chemical signals 71
salicylate antioxidant 205
saline solution, as treatment 54
saliva test for cancer 136
Salmonella bacteria 11, 90a, 195
Santa, and reindeer shortfall 47
sarcasm 85a
Saturn (planet) 198

scent (trail) 34
schizophrenia 62, 168
scratch, in paintwork 53b
scratch-resistant coating 29, 53b
scrotum, temperature sensitivity 131
sculpture, detecting fake 77
sea food allergies 212a
sea hare, Californian 50f
sea saltiness 45f
sea wall, relatively porous 199
sea water analysis 23
sedimentary rocks 4
self-replicating robot 97a
setae (tiny hairs) 118b
shape-memory polymers (SMPs) 197
shaving, and health 153f
Shigella bacteria 195
shoes 13a
sight, restoration of 225
silica particles 29
silicon 122b
silicon carbide, as petrified wood 170
skin cells, and ageing 169a
skin cells for skin grafts 218
skin tissue regeneration 218
skull, the 25
sleep 24b, 52, 81b
Sleepsmart waking device 81b
slug, world's biggest 50f
slug and snail removal 82

smell, sense of 16, 34, 113b, 168

smell, sense of, in insects 141, 172

smog-monitoring pigeons 124

smoking cigarettes, effects of 93, 109f, 150b

smoking cigarettes, giving up/quitting 190

snails, migrating 32

'snapper', seabed wavepower 159

snooze button 3a

snow, whiteness of 37b

soccer 1

solar cell technology 70, 122a

solar electricity generation 108

solar panels 70

solar-powered handbag 155b

Sonic Hedgehog gene 14

sound 18

sound-sensitive lighting 145b

sound waves 2f

South Atlantic Anomaly, the 80

space cycle 12a

spark plugs 120f

species, origination of new 87

spectral analysis as medical diagnostic 195

speed trap using the Doppler shift 219

sperm count and scrotal temperature 131

sperm whales, and the bends 66

spider-web silk, synthetic 125b

spin cycle, washtub's 150a

spinning ball(s) 1

spy-plane, robot/unmanned 111a

Staphylococcus aureus bacteria 210

star, exiting the Galaxy 179a

star, near by, with planets 217

star, very distant 91

stardust and the *Stardust* project 119, 134

Steadicopter, unmanned helicopter 111a

stem cells, foetal 21

stem cells, non-foetal 102

stem cell therapy 161, 179b, 189b, 194a

stimulants 24b

stomach, nerve activity in 155a

storytellers 3b, 160f

Streptomyces platensis bacteria 224

stress, effects of 44

stroke 93, 135b, 169b, 226

stun-guns, laser-operated 149

subdural haematomas 25

suggestion, power of 41

suicide, reason for 19a

sulphuric acid 33f

Sun Trap solar power system 155b
'superbug' infections 210
'supertasters' 76f
surgery by microrobots 157
surgical implants in humans 81a, 225
suspended animation 148
Swedish poetry 69a
SWIFT satellite 91

tail-wagging, dogs' 85b
talking chimps 138
tars in cigarettes 109f
taste, sense of 16
taste buds, extra 76f
tattoo, erasable 221
tea, as preventative medicine 90a
team colours, effects of 94
television *see* TV
temperature, water 40f
temporal lobe of the brain 59
temptation, effects of 123
termite infestation 126
terpenoids 48a
testosterone 56
textiles that change colour 180
text messaging, as voicemail 143
text messaging, with animation 118a
text messaging, with ring tones 128a
theta waves in the brain 154

three-dimensional 'screen' 116
throat cancer 136
thrombin, blood-clotting agent 182
thyroid disease(s) 21
toast from a toaster 115
tobacco in cigarettes 109f
tobacco plants, signal recipients 71
tonsils, and bad breath 109
tooth decay, drill-less treatment 96
tornadoes in Europe 208f
torrent frog, concave-eared 156
Tourette's syndrome 62
trademark 14
train, approaching 15f
trans-fatty acids 99
transplant of an ovary 214
tree-nesting ants 88
triglycerides, effects in the diet of 99
tritium radoactive decay 122b
tropomyosin protein 212a
tumour and tumour cells 46, 51, 136, 177, 201
turmeric, as treatment 67
TV adverts 35b
TV programmes 35b, 90b
Tyrannosaurus rex 38, 76

ultrasound technology 39, 178
umbilical cord 8
unmanned aerial vehicle (UAV) 111a

urine specimen, as
diagnostic 220

vaccine 5, 188
Vega (α Lyrae) 69a
vegetables, dislike of eating
76f
vegetarian-friendly 'meat'
203
vegetarianism, and the
environment 48b
vein, locating 39, 128, 178
veinfinder 39
Velcro 14
Venus flytrap, mechanism
174
Vick (Vick's VapoRub™)
143f
video clips 10
videophones 118a
village weaverbird, African
160
viral infection, in humans
163f, 188, 195
virtual funerals 13b
viruses, in animals/birds
58a, 121
viruses, drug-resistant 137a
viruses, scanning for 100,
195
visibility for cyclists 30b
visually impaired, help for
the 103a
voicemail labelling system
162
Voice-SMS technology
143
volatile vapour in fuel tank
37a

voting device 27a

walking, styles of 133f
warm-blooded mammals
61f
washing 6a
water, bottled 69b
water, cold, 147f
water, hot 40f, 147f
water, tap 69b
water analysis 35a
water on Mars 27b
water-repellent coating 33
waves and electricity
generation 159
weather forecasting 23, 36,
215
weather monitoring 122b
wedding rings, bone 128b
weight change 40f
weight training 75b
white blood cells 5
Whitelee wind farm 206b
WiFi links 2
wind farm, in Scotland
206b
wine bottle, speaking 40
wineglasses and
discoloration 37b
woman's weighing up a
man 61
wound dressing, double-
action 182

X-rays 6b, 9, 77

yeast(s) 208

Zbtb7 gene 14

zebra crossing, portable
  113a
zero gravity 12a

3-methyl-2-octanoic acid 7
6-methyl-5-heptene-2-one
  196